Introduction To General, Organic, & Biochemistry In The Laboratory, 10th Edition

General Chemistry - Inorganic

Author

Hein

ISBN 9781119928362

Printed in the United States of America 10 9 8 7 6 5 4 3 2

List of Titles

Introduction to General, Organic, and Biochemistry in the Laboratory, 10th edition
by Morris Hein, Judith N. Peisen, and James M. Ritchey
Copyright © 2012, ISBN: 978-0-470-59881-8

Table of Contents

INTRODUCTION TO GENERAL, ORGANIC, AND BIOCHEMISTRY IN THE LABORATORY

TENTH EDITION

Morris Hein
Mount San Antonio College

Judith N. Peisen
Hagerstown Community College

James M. Ritchey
California State University at Sacramento

WILEY

JOHN WILEY & SONS, INC.

Founded in 1807, John Wiley & Sons, Inc. has been a valued source of knowledge and understanding for more than 200 years, helping people around the world meet their needs and fulfill their aspirations. Our company is built on a foundation of principles that include responsibility to the communities we serve and where we live and work. In 2008, we launched a Corporate Citizenship Initiative, a global effort to address the environmental, social, economic, and ethical challenges we face in our business. Among the issues we are addressing are carbon impact, paper specifications and procurement, ethical conduct within our business and among our vendors, and community and charitable support. For more information, please visit our website: www.wiley.com/go/citizenship.

Evaluation copies are provided to qualified academics and professionals for review purposes only, for use in their courses during the next academic year. These copies are licensed and may not be sold or transferred to a third party. Upon completion of the review period, please return the evaluation copy to Wiley. Return instructions and a free of charge return shipping label are available at **www.wiley.com/go/returnlabel**. If you have chosen to adopt this textbook for use in your course, please accept this book as your complimentary desk copy. Outside of the United States, please contact your local representative.

ISBN 978-0470-59881-8

Printed in the United States of America

10   9   8   7   6   5   4   3   2   1

Printed and bound by Integrated Book Technologies.

Preface

This manual is intended for the student with little or no previous coursework in chemistry who is usually enrolled in a two-semester chemistry sequence for non-majors, often preparing for careers in allied health programs such as nursing, radiography, medical lab technician, etc. The experiments begin with very simple laboratory techniques, measurements, physical and chemical properties, and calculations needed by beginning students in a foundations course and progress to relatively complex procedures typical of General Chemistry students. The last sixteen experiments provide a sequence of organic chemistry and biochemistry experiments. The number and variety of experiments provide the instructor with reasonable flexibility in preparing a laboratory schedule to support and complement the course lecture topics for students of varying previous experience with chemistry.

Our major objectives of this flexible laboratory program are to provide experience with (1) hands-on laboratory experimentation, (2) the capabilities and limitations of measurements, (3) a variety of chemical reactions and the equations used to describe them, (4) the collection, analysis, and graphing of data, (5) responsible disposal of chemicals for personal and environmental health, (6) Using a computer for graphing of data, (7) drawing valid conclusions from experimental evidence, and (8) support and reinforcement of concepts introduced in the lecture component of the course.

We have tried to maintain a balance between descriptive and quantitative experiments at all levels of a non-majors course (introductory, general chem., organic/biochem). Nine experiments provide experience with physical properties of matter; ten experiments include unknowns for student analysis, and nine provide opportunities for graphing data. All experiments emphasize basic skills and data analysis. The instructor's manual provides sample student data, including graphs, for most experiments.

The format is designed to be helpful and convenient for both student and instructor and includes the following features:

1. A concise discussion of the basic underlying principles for each experiment provides pertinent background material to supplement, not replace, the textbook.

2. Six Study Aids provide supplementary material common to several experiments on the important topics of (a) significant figures, (b) chemical formulas and equations, (c) reading and preparing graphs by hand and by computer, (d) use of a scientific calculator, (e) Dimensional Analysis and Stoichiometry, and (f) introduction to organic chemistry.

3. Experimental procedures have been extensively tested by many students and provide enough detail for students to work with only general supervision.

4. Report forms for each experiment are cross-referenced to letters and subtitles in the procedure, designed to be completed before leaving the lab session, and relatively easy to grade.

5. The names and formulas of reagents used are listed at the beginning of each experiment.

6. Special safety precautions and waste disposal instructions are indicated when necessary at the point where they are required within the procedure.

7. For the convenience of the instructor and stockroom personnel, the appendices provide (a) an experiment-by-experiment list of special equipment and preparations needed, (b) a list of suggested equipment for student lockers, (c) an experiment-by-experiment list of waste disposal instructions, (d) a list of suggested auxiliary equipment, and (e) a complete list of reagents and details for the preparation of solutions.

8. The lab manual also contains 26 Exercises, many of which can be used as supplements for a number of experiments. Exercises 25 and 26 (Molecular Models and Isomerism and Stereoisomerism—Optical Activity) may be used as experiments to give students hands-on experience in these subjects.

The experiment which is new to the Tenth Edition is Experiment 8, Water, Solutions, and pH. This experiment provides an introduction to the properties of water especially important in the life sciences, introduces some skills used in biotechnology and the concept of molarity. This new experiment is an excellent foundation for Experiment 9, Properties of Solutions which is found in previous editions. Properties of Lead (II), Silver, and Mercury (I) Ions (Experiment 14 in the twelfth edition) which involved the use of heavy metal cations, has been eliminated.

Meticulous instructions for waste disposal have been continued and updated for students within each procedure and in the Instructor's Manual. The instructions for Preparing a Graph (Study Aid 3) have been updated to the most recent version of Excel (2007).

We are especially indebted to students in the chemistry departments of Mount San Antonio College and Hagerstown Community College for their patience and helpful suggestions during the development and testing of this laboratory program. We appreciate the feedback from instructors and students at the many schools over the years that have used this lab manual in their introductory chemistry course. A special thanks to Dr. Richard Montgomery, Dr. William Elliott, and Dr. Melanie Ulrich for their contribution to the Water, Solutions, and pH experiment that is new to this edition. Further suggestions for improvements of material in this laboratory manual are always welcome.

Morris Hein
Judith N. Peisen
James M. Ritchey

To the Student

Since your laboratory time is limited, it is important to come to each session prepared by at least one hour of detailed study of the scheduled experiment. This should be considered a standing homework assignment.

Each of the experiments in this manual is composed of four parts:

1. **Materials and Equipment**—a list that includes the formulas of all substances used in each experiment.

2. **Discussion**—a brief discussion of the principles underlying the experiment.

3. **Procedure**—detailed directions for performing the experiment with safety precautions clearly noted and disposal procedures for chemical waste provided throughout and identified by a waste icon.

4. **Report for Experiment**—a form for recording data and observations, performing calculations, and answering questions.

Follow the directions in the procedure carefully, and consult your instructor if you have any questions. For convenience, the letters and subtitles in the report form have been set up to correspond with those in the procedure section of each experiment.

As you make your observations and obtain your data, record them on the report form. Try to use your time efficiently; when a reaction or process is occurring that takes considerable time and requires little watching, start working on other parts of the experiment, perform calculations, answer questions on the report form, or clean up your equipment.

Except when your instructor directs otherwise, you should do all the work individually. You may profit by discussing experimental results with your classmates, but in the final analysis you must rely on your own observations and judgment in completing the report form.

⚠ Safety Guidelines

While in the chemistry laboratory, you are responsible not only for your own safety but for the safety of everyone else. *We have included safety precautions in every experiment where needed, and they are highlighted with the icon shown in the title of this section.* Your instructor may modify these instructions and give you more specific directions on safety in your laboratory. If the proper precautions and techniques are used, none of the experiments in this laboratory program are hazardous. But without your reading and following the instructions, without knowledge about handling and disposal of chemicals, and without the use of common sense at all times, accidents can happen. Even when everyone is doing his or her best to comply with the safety guidelines in each experiment, accidents can happen. It is your responsibility to minimize these accidents and know what to do if they happen.

Laboratory Rules and Safety Procedures

1. **Wear protective goggles or glasses** at all times in the laboratory work area. These glasses should wrap around the face so liquids cannot splash into the eye from the side. These goggles are mandated by eye-protection laws and are not optional, even though they may be uncomfortable. Contact lenses increase the risk of problems with eye safety, even when protective goggles are worn. If you wear contact lenses, inform the instructor.

2. **Dress appropriately** for the laboratory. Shoes that do not completely cover the feet are not allowed *(no sandals)*. Long hair should be tied back. Wear a laboratory coat or apron, if available, to protect your clothing.

3. **Keep your benchtop organized as you work.** Put jackets, book bags, and personal belongings away from the work areas. Before you leave, clean your work area and make sure the gas and water are turned off. Clean and return all glassware and equipment to your drawer or the lab bench where you borrowed it.

4. **Keep all stock bottles of solid and liquid reagents in the dispensing area.** Do not bring reagent bottles to your laboratory work area. Use test tubes, beakers, or weigh boats to obtain chemicals from the dispensing areas: (1) the reagent shelf, (2) the balance tables, (3) under the fume hood, and (4) as instructed.

5. **Keep the balance and the area around it clean.** Do not place chemicals directly on the balance pans; place a piece of weighing paper, a weigh boat, or another small container on the pan first, and then weigh your material. **Never weigh an object while it is hot.**

6. **Check the labels on every reagent bottle carefully.** Many names and formulas appear similar at first glance. Label every beaker, test tube, etc., into which you transfer chemicals. Many labels will contain the National Fire Protection Association (NFPA) diamond label, which provides information about the flammability, reactivity, health effects, and miscellaneous effects for the substance. Each hazard is rated 0 (least hazardous) to 4 (most hazardous). For example, the NFPA label for potassium chromate is shown below.

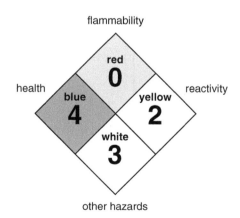

More specific information (the reason for potassium chromate being rated an extreme health hazard, for example) about all known substances is available in the form of Material Safety Data Sheets (MSDS), which many institutions keep on file for chemicals stored and used in their laboratories. MSDSs are usually provided with chemicals by the supplier when they are purchased and are easily obtained from many website sources. Because of its hazardous nature, chromates have been removed from this lab manual.

7. **Never return unused chemicals to the reagent bottles.** This is a source of possible contamination of the entire stock bottle. Dispose of unused chemicals exactly as instructed in the waste disposal instructions for that substance, identified by throughout each experiment.

8. **Disposal of wastes must follow state and federal guidelines.** Do not put anything into the trash or sink without thinking first. We have tried to anticipate every disposal decision in the procedure and marked the procedure with the waste icon. The following guidelines are the foundation of waste disposal decisions:

   a. Broken glass is put into a clearly marked special container.

   b. Organic solvents are never poured into the sink. They are usually flammable and often immiscible with water. Instead, they are poured into a specially marked container ("waste organic solvents") provided when needed.

   c. Solutions containing cations and anions considered toxic by the EPA are never poured into the sink. They are poured into specially marked containers ("waste heavy metal," etc.) provided when needed. The name of all ions disposed of into a specific bottle must be listed on the label.

   d. Solutions poured in the sink should be washed down with plenty of water.

   e. Some solid chemicals must also be disposed of in specially labeled containers. If you are not sure what to do, ask the instructor.

   f. Each school may have its own policy for waste disposal which supercedes the instructions in this manual.

9. **Avoid contaminating stock solutions.** Do not insert medicine droppers or pipets into reagent bottles containing liquids. Instead, pour a little of the liquid into a small beaker or test tube. If the bottle is fitted with a special pipet that is stored with the bottle, this may not be necessary.

10. **Avoid all direct contact with chemicals.**

    a. Wash your hands anytime you get chemicals on them and at the end of the laboratory session.

    b. If you spill something, clean it up immediately before it dries or gets on your papers or skin.

    c. **Never** pipet by mouth.

    d. **Never** eat, drink, or smoke in the laboratory.

    e. Do not look down into the open end of a test tube in which a reaction is being conducted, and do not point the open end of a test tube at someone else.

    f. Inhale odors and chemicals with great caution. Waft vapors toward your nose. The fume hood will be used for all irritating and toxic vapors.

11. **Working with glass requires special precautions:**

    a. Do not heat graduated cylinders, burets, pipets, or bottles with a burner flame.

    b. Do not hold a test tube or beaker in your hand during a chemical reaction.

c. Do not touch glass that has been near a flame or hot plate. Hot glass looks the same as cool glass and may cause serious burns.

d. Learn and practice proper procedures when inserting glass tubing into rubber stoppers. (See Experiment 1)

12. **Learn the location and proper use of safety equipment:** fire extinguisher, eye wash, first aid kit, fire blanket, safety shower, spill kits, and other equipment available.

13. **Never work alone** in the laboratory area.

14. **Report all accidents** to the instructor, no matter how minor.

15. **Do not perform unauthorized experiments.**

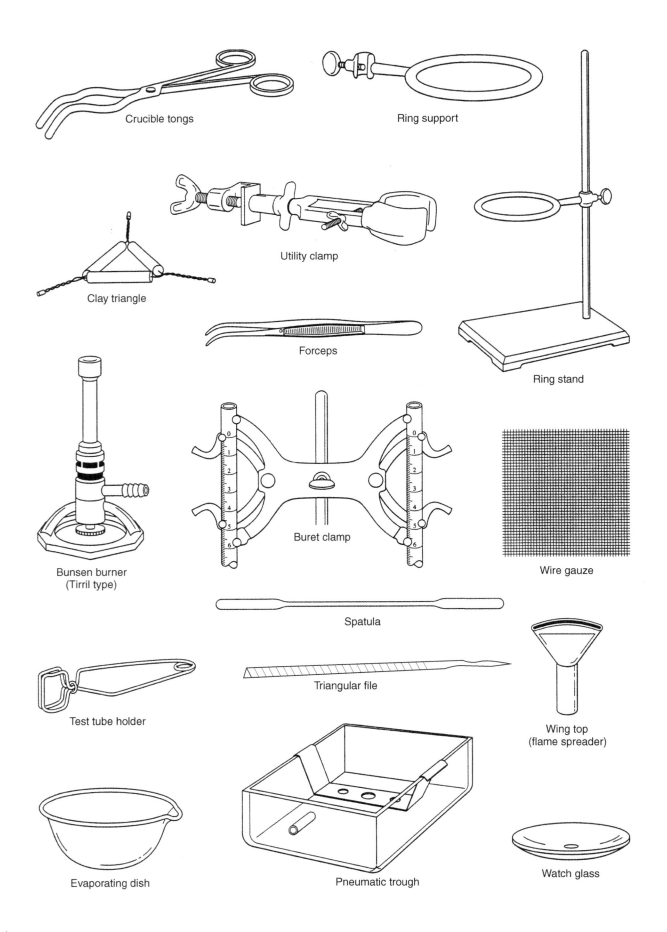

Crucible tongs

Ring support

Utility clamp

Clay triangle

Forceps

Ring stand

Bunsen burner
(Tirril type)

Buret clamp

Wire gauze

Spatula

Test tube holder

Triangular file

Wing top
(flame spreader)

Evaporating dish

Pneumatic trough

Watch glass

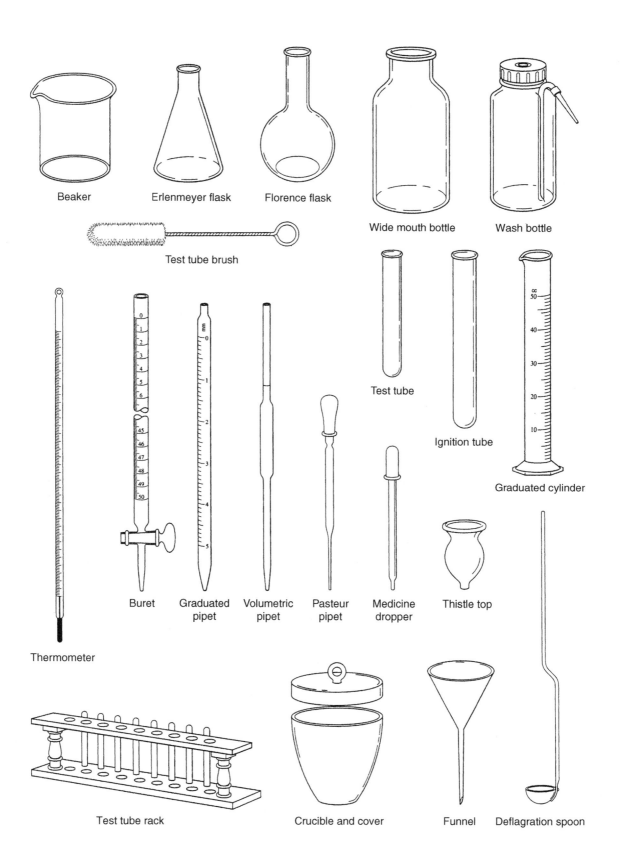

Beaker

Erlenmeyer flask

Florence flask

Wide mouth bottle

Wash bottle

Test tube brush

Test tube

Ignition tube

Graduated cylinder

Thermometer

Buret

Graduated pipet

Volumetric pipet

Pasteur pipet

Medicine dropper

Thistle top

Test tube rack

Crucible and cover

Funnel

Deflagration spoon

EXPERIMENT 1

Laboratory Techniques

MATERIALS AND EQUIPMENT

Solids: lead(II) iodide (PbI_2), sodium nitrate ($NaNO_3$), and sodium chloride ($NaCl$). **Liquid:** glycerol. **Solutions:** 0.1 M lead(II) nitrate [$Pb(NO_3)_2$] and 0.1 M sodium iodide (NaI). Ceramfab pad, 100 mL and 400 mL beakers, Bunsen burner, No. 1 evaporating dish, triangular file, funnel, wire gauze, filter paper, glass rod, clay triangle, 6 mm glass tubing, wing top (flame spreader).

DISCUSSION AND PROCEDURE

Wear protective glasses.

A.   Laboratory Burners

Almost all laboratory burners used today are modifications of a design by the German chemist Robert Bunsen. In Bunsen's fundamental design, also widely used in domestic and industrial gas burners, gas and air are premixed by admitting the gas at relatively high velocity from a jet in the base of the burner. This rapidly moving stream of gas causes air to be drawn into the barrel from side ports and to mix with the gas before entering the combustion zone at the top of the burner.

The burner is connected to a gas cock by a short length of rubber or plastic tubing. With some burners the gas cock is turned to the **fully on** position when the burner is in use, and the amount of gas admitted to the burner is controlled by adjusting a needle valve in the base of the burner. In burners that do not have this needle valve, the gas flow is regulated by partly opening or closing the gas cock. With either type of burner **the gas should always be turned off at the gas cock when the burner is not in use** (to avoid possible dangerous gas leakage from the needle valve or old tubing).

1. **Operation of the Burner.**   Examine the construction of your burner (Figure 1.1) and familiarize yourself with its operation. A burner is usually lighted with the air inlet ports nearly closed. The ports are closed by rotating the barrel of the burner in a clockwise direction. After the gas has been turned on and lighted, the size and quality of the flame is adjusted by admitting air and regulating the flow of gas. Air is admitted by rotating the barrel; gas is regulated with the needle valve, if present, or the gas cock. Insufficient air will cause a luminous yellow, smoky flame; too much air will cause the flame to be noisy and possibly blow out. A Bunsen burner flame that is satisfactory for most purposes is shown in Figure 1.2; such a flame is said to be "nonluminous." Note that the hottest region is immediately above the bright blue cone of a well-adjusted flame.

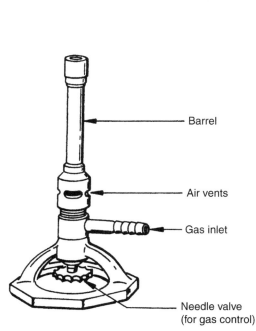

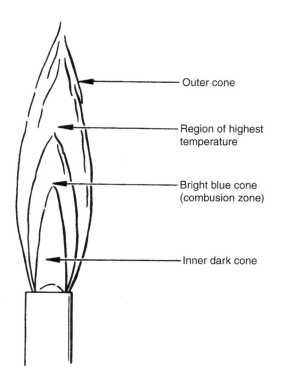

Outer cone

Region of highest temperature

Bright blue cone (combusion zone)

Inner dark cone

Barrel

Air vents

Gas inlet

Needle valve (for gas control)

Figure 1.1   Bunsen burner (Tirrill type)

Figure 1.2   Bunsen burner flame

B. Glassworking

 Dispose of broken and nonusable glass in the container provided.

In laboratory work it is often necessary to fabricate simple items of equipment, making use of glass tubing and rubber stoppers. In working with glass tubing, improper techniques may result not only in an unsatisfactory apparatus but also in severe cuts and burns. Therefore the numbered instructions below should be studied carefully. Prepare the following list of items (illustrated in Figure 1.3), using 6 millimeter (mm) glass tubing and rod.

Two straight tubes, one 24 centimeters (cm) long, the other 12 cm (Figure 1.3A).

Two right-angle bends (Figure 1.3B).

One delivery tube (Figure 1.3C).

Two buret tips (Figure 1.3D). (Optional)

One stirring rod if there is none in your locker (Figure 1.3E).

This equipment will be used in future experiments. After it has been completed and approved by your instructor, store them in your locker.

1. **Cutting Glass Tubing.**   (See Figure 1.4.) Mark the tube with a pencil or ball-point pen at the point where it is to be cut. Grasp the tubing about 1 cm from the mark and hold it in position on the laboratory table. Hold the file by the tang (or handle) end and, pressing the edge of the file firmly against the glass at right angles to the tubing, make a scratch on the tubing by pushing the file away from you. If the file is in good condition a single stroke should suffice. Several strokes may be required if the file is dull, but if more than one stroke is needed, all must follow the same path so that only one scratch mark is present on the tubing. The scratch need not be very deep or very long, but it should be clearly defined.

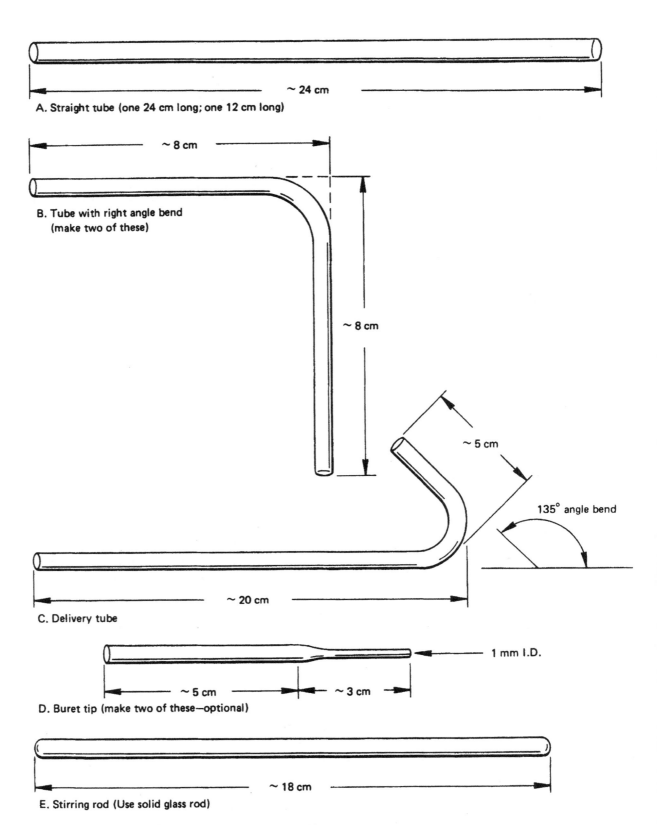

A. Straight tube (one 24 cm long; one 12 cm long)

~ 24 cm

~ 8 cm

B. Tube with right angle bend
   (make two of these)

~ 8 cm

~ 5 cm

135° angle bend

~ 20 cm

C. Delivery tube

1 mm I.D.

~ 5 cm   ~ 3 cm

D. Buret tip (make two of these—optional)

~ 18 cm

E. Stirring rod (Use solid glass rod)

Figure 1.3   Glassware (Illustrations are not to scale)

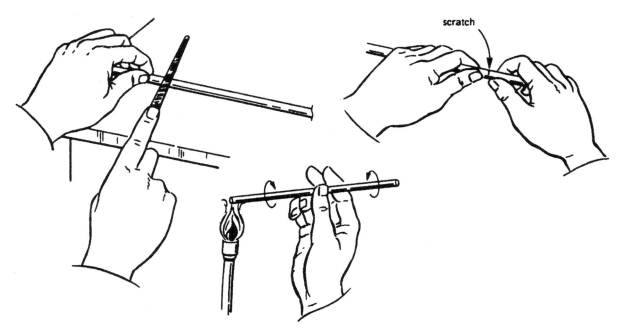

Figure 1.4   Cutting and fire-polishing glass tubing

Grasp the tubing with your thumbs together directly opposite the scratch mark (see Figure 1.4). Now apply pressure with the thumbs as though bending the ends toward your body while at the same time exerting a slight pull on the tubing. A straight, clean break should result. Use the flat side of your file to remove any sharp projections from the ends of the cut tubing. After cutting glass in this way, the ends of the cut glass, although clean and flat, are still very sharp and must be fire-polished in order to avoid personal injury.

2. Fire-Polishing Glass.   **Fire polishing** is the process of removing the sharp edges of glass by heating the tubing in a burner flame.

While continuously rotating the tubing, heat the end in the hottest part of the flame until the sharp edges are smooth. Be careful not to heat too much because the opening will become constricted. When the fire-polishing is completed, remember that the glass is **hot** even though it looks cool.

 Put the hot glass tubing on a Ceramfab pad to cool. This is an excellent safety device. If hot objects are always placed on the pad and allowed to cool, then picked up with caution, one is less likely to get burned. The Ceramfab pad also protects the hot glass from sudden chilling (thermal shock) and the table top from injury.

Your instructor will have some examples of properly fire-polished tubing available for your inspection. Laboratory stirring rods are easily made by cutting glass rod in the same way described for tubing and fire-polishing the ends until they are smooth and rounded.

Whenever glass is cut it must be fire-polished in order to avoid personal injury.

3. Bending Glass Tubing.   Put the wing top (flame spreader) on your burner and adjust the flame so that a sharply defined region of intense blue color is visible. Grasp the tubing to be bent at both ends and hold it in the flame lengthwise just above the zone of intense blue color. Continuously rotate the tubing in the flame until it has softened enough to bend easily

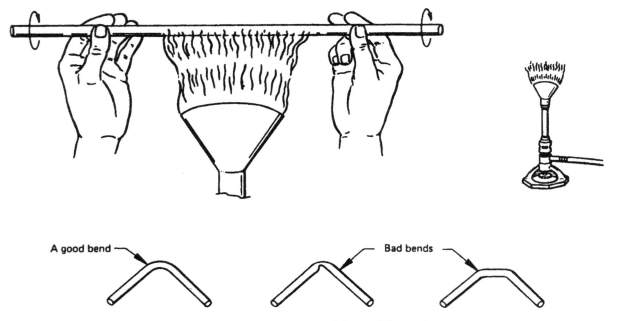

Figure 1.5   Heating glass tubing with a wing top

 (Figure 1.5). Remove the tubing from the flame, bend to the desired shape, and set aside to cool on the Ceramfab pad. If the bend is not satisfactory, discard the glass in the container provided and repeat the work with a new piece.

If a bend is to be made where one arm of tubing is too short to hold in the hand while heating (Figure 1.3C), follow one of two procedures: (1) Proceed as in the above paragraph, using enough tubing to handle it from both ends; then cut to size and firepolish it after the bend is completed. (2) Heat a piece of tubing of proper size, holding it at one end and rotating it until it is soft in the region to be bent; then remove it from the flame and bend by grasping with tongs or by inserting the tang of a file into the hot end of the tubing.

4. **Preparing Buret Tips (Jets).**   A buret tip (or jet) (Figure 1.3D) is prepared as follows: Remove the wing top and heat a small section in the center of a 14 cm length of tubing while rotating it in the hottest portion of the burner flame (without wing top) until the tubing is very soft. Remove from the flame and slowly pull the ends away from each other while holding the tubing in a vertical position. After cooling, cut the tips to the desired dimensions. Fire-polish all edges.

5. **Inserting Glass Tubing into a Stopper.**

⚠ If the glass tubing is held in the wrong place during its insertion into a stopper, serious injury can occur if the tubing shatters or breaks and pushes into the hand. Read the following instructions carefully.

Lubricate the hole in the stopper with glycerol (glycerine), using a stirring rod to make sure that the lubricant actually gets into the hole. Grasp the fire-polished tubing about 1 cm from the end to be inserted. Holding the lubricated stopper in the other hand, start the tubing into the hole by gently twisting it, and gradually work it all the way through the stopper. Be sure to grip the tubing at a point not more than 1 cm from the stopper at all times when making the insertion. Gripping at greater distances and twisting will break the tubing and probably cause personal injury. It is also good safety practice to protect your hands with a towel when inserting or removing glass tubing from rubber stoppers.

The end of the tube should protrude at least 5 mm from the stopper, so that the free passage of fluids is not prevented by flaps of rubber. After insertion make sure that the tube is not plugged, and remove the excess glycerol either by washing or with a towel. Note the lubricating properties of glycerol by rubbing a drop between your thumb and forefinger.

3. **Removing Glass Tubing from Stoppers.** Tubing should be removed from stoppers at the end of the laboratory period. Be careful to grip the tubing at a point very close to the stopper when twisting. If allowed to stand for several days the stopper may stick to the glass and be difficult to remove. In the event of sticking, do not use "strong arm" methods. A cork borer (No. 3 for 6 mm tubing) may be inserted between the rubber and glass to help remove the tubing from the stopper, but consult your instructor before attempting this procedure.

C. Evaporation

Evaporation is one of the processes used to separate a dissolved solid from a liquid.

1. Prepare the simple water bath illustrated in Figure 1.6. Before placing the beaker into position be sure the hottest part of the burner flame will reach the bottom of the beaker. Put the beaker of tap water on the wire gauze and begin heating.

2. **Preparing the Solution.** Cover the bottom of a 150 mm (standard) test tube with a small quantity of sodium chloride. Add distilled water until the test tube is about one-quarter full and stir with a glass rod until the salt is dissolved.

3. **Evaporating the Solution.** Pour the sodium chloride solution into an evaporating dish. Place the evaporating dish on the beaker of water being heated. Continue heating the water to maintain boiling— replenishing if necessary—until all of the water has evaporated from the solution in the evaporating dish, leaving the original solid as the residue.

4. Dissolve the residue with tap water and flush the salt solution down the sink.

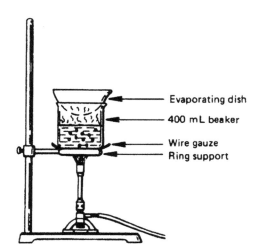

Evaporating dish
400 mL beaker
Wire gauze
Ring support

WASTE DISPOSE OF PROPERLY

Figure 1.6   Evaporation on a simple water bath

D. Filtration

The process of separating suspended insoluble solids from liquids by means of filters is called **filtration.** Insoluble solids, called **precipitates,** are formed during some chemical reactions. In the laboratory these precipitates are generally separated from the solutions by filtering them out on a paper filter. The liquid that passes through the filter paper is the **filtrate;** the solid precipitate remaining on the filter paper is the **residue.**

1. **Forming a Precipitate.** Fill a test tube about one-quarter full of lead(II) nitrate solution. Fill a second tube about one-half full of sodium iodide solution. These solutions contain lead(II) nitrate and sodium iodide, each dissolved in water. Pour the lead(II) nitrate solution into a 100 milliliter (mL) beaker. Slowly pour the sodium iodide solution into the beaker,

stir, and observe the results. The chemical reaction that occurred formed sodium nitrate and lead(II) iodide. One of these products is a yellow precipitate.

   2. **Filtering the Products.**   Prepare a filter as shown in Figure 1.7.

   (a) Fold a circle of filter paper in half. Fold in half again and open out into a cone. Tear off one corner of the outside folded edge. The top edge of the cone which is to touch the glass funnel should not be torn.

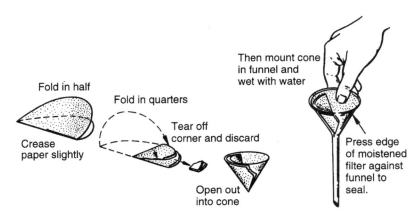

Figure 1.7   Folding and mounting filter paper

   (b) Fit the opened cone into a short-stemmed funnel, placing the torn edge next to the glass. Wet with distilled water and press the top edge of the paper against the funnel, forming a seal. Use one of the setups suggested in Figure 1.8 for supporting the funnel. Then, stir the mixture of products in the small beaker with a stirring rod and slowly pour it down the stirring rod into the filter paper in the funnel (see Figure 1.9). Do not overfill the paper filter cone.

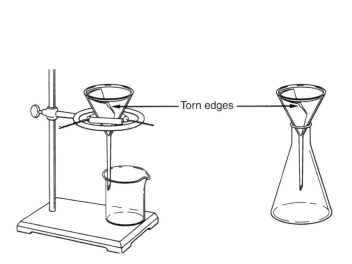

**Figure 1.8   Support the filter with a ring stand
or an Erlenmeyer flask**

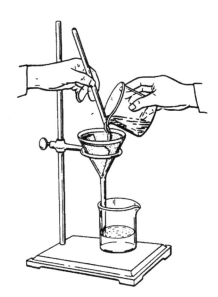

**Figure 1.9   Pouring a solution
down a stirring rod**

3. **Identification of the Precipitate.** After the filtration is completed, compare the residue with the samples of solid sodium nitrate and lead(II) iodide provided by the instructor to determine which of these is the residue on the filter paper.

4. Use forceps to remove the filter paper with the precipitate and transfer it into the waste jar provided. Pour the filtrate into the waste bottle provided. Rinse the reaction beaker and the test tubes with water and pour the rinse solutions into the waste bottle.

WASTE
DISPOSE OF
PROPERLY

5. Review the safety procedures for chemical waste disposal in the preface to determine the specific reasons for putting the waste into special containers rather than the trash and the sink.

NAME _____

SECTION _____ DATE _____

INSTRUCTOR _____

REPORT FOR EXPERIMENT 1

Laboratory Techniques

A, B.   Laboratory Burners and Glassworking

Glassware shown in Figure 1.3

Articles	Instructor's Check and Comments
Straight tubes (2)	
Right-angle bends (2)	
Delivery tube (1)	
Buret tips (2)	(optional)
Stirring rod (1)	

Instructor's OK or grade on glass work _____

QUESTIONS AND PROBLEMS

1. Why is it necessary to turn off the gas with the gas cock rather than with the valve on the burner?

2. Why is air mixed with gas in the barrel of the burner before the gas is burned?

3. How would you adjust a burner which

   (a) has a yellow and smoky flame?

   (b) is noisy with a tendency to blow itself out?

4. Why are glass tubes and rods always fire-polished after cutting?

5. Explain briefly how to insert glass tubing into a rubber stopper.

6. Name the lubricant used for inserting glass tubing in rubber stoppers.

_____

C. Evaporation

Give the name and formula of the residue remaining after evaporation:

Name_____ Formula _____

D. Filtration

1. What is the name, formula, and color of the precipitate recovered by filtration?

Name _____ Formula _____ Color _____

2. Explain why the filter paper with the precipitate is collected in a jar instead of thrown into the trash can? (Refer to the section on waste disposal in Laboratory Rules and Safety Practices.)

3. Give the names and formulas of two compounds that must be present in the filtrate.

Name _____ Formula _____

Name _____ Formula _____

EXPERIMENT 2

Measurements

MATERIALS AND EQUIPMENT

Solids: sodium chloride (NaCl) and ice. Balance, ruler, thermometer, solid object for density determination, No. 1 or 2 solid rubber stopper.

DISCUSSION

Chemistry is an experimental science, and measurements are fundamental to most of the experiments. It is important to learn how to make and use these measurements properly.

The SI System of Units

The International System of Units (*Systeme Internationale, SI*) or metric system is a decimal system of units for measurements used almost exclusively in science. It is built around a set of units including the meter, the gram, and the liter and uses factors of 10 to express larger or smaller multiples of these units. To express larger or smaller units, prefixes are added to the names of the units. Deci, centi, and milli are units that are 1/10, 1/100, and 1/1000, respectively, of these units. The most common of these prefixes with their corresponding values expressed as decimals and powers of 10 are shown in the table below.

Prefix	Decimal Equivalent	Power of 10	Examples
deci (d)	0.1	10^{-1}	$1\ dg = 0.1\ g = 10^{-1}\ g$
centi (c)	0.01	10^{-2}	$1\ cm = 0.01\ m = 10^{-2}\ m$
milli (m)	0.001	10^{-3}	$1\ mg = 0.001\ g = 10^{-3}\ g$
kilo (k)	1000	10^{3}	$1\ km = 1000\ m = 10^{3}\ m$

Dimensional Analysis

It will often be necessary to convert from the American System of units to the SI system or to convert units within the SI system. Conversion factors are available from tables (see Appendix 4) or can be developed from the metric prefixes and their corresponding values as shown in the table above. Dimensional analysis, a problem-solving method with many applications in chemistry, is very valuable for converting one unit to another by the use of conversion factors. A review of using dimensional analysis for converting units is provided here. Study Aid 5 provides more help with this problem-solving tool.

Conversion Factors come from equivalent relationships, usually stated as equations. From each equivalence statement two conversion factors can be written in fractional form with a value of 1. For example:

Equivalence Equations	Conversion Factor #1	Conversion Factor #2
1 dollar = 4 quarters	$\dfrac{1 \text{ dollar}}{4 \text{ quarters}}$	$\dfrac{4 \text{ quarters}}{1 \text{ dollar}}$
1 lb = 453.6 g	$\dfrac{1 \text{ lb}}{453.6 \text{ g}}$	$\dfrac{453.6 \text{ g}}{1 \text{ lb}}$
1 mm = 10^{-3} m	$\dfrac{1 \text{ mm}}{10^{-3}\text{m}}$	$\dfrac{10^{-3}\text{m}}{1 \text{ mm}}$
1 ns = 10^{-9} s	$\dfrac{1 \text{ ns}}{10^{-9}\text{s}}$	$\dfrac{10^{-9}\text{s}}{1 \text{ ns}}$

The dimensional analysis method of converting units involves organizing one or more conversion factors into a logical series which cancels or eliminates all units except the unit(s) wanted in the answer.

For example: To convert 2.53 lb into milligrams (mg), the setup is:

$$(2.53 \text{ lb})\left(\frac{453.6 \text{ g}}{1 \text{ lb}}\right)\left(\frac{1 \text{ mg}}{10^{-3}\text{g}}\right) = 1.15 \times 10^6 \text{ mg}$$

Note, that in completing this calculation, units are treated as numbers, **lb** in the denominator is canceled into **lb** in the numerator and **g** in the denominator is cancelled into **g** in the numerator. More examples of unit conversions can be found in Study Aid 5.

Although the SI unit of temperature is the Kelvin (K), the Celsius (or centigrade) temperature scale is commonly used in scientific work and the Fahrenheit scale is commonly used in this country. On the Celsius scale the freezing point of water is designated 0°C, the boiling point 100°C.

Precision and Accuracy of Measurements

Scientific measurements must be as **precise** as possible. This means that every measurement will include one uncertain or estimated digit. When making measurements we normally estimate between the smallest scale divisions on the instrument being used. Then, only the uncertain digit should vary if the measurement is repeated using the same instrument, even if it is repeated by someone else. The **accuracy** of a measurement or calculated quantity refers to its agreement with some known value. For example, we need to make two measurements, volume and mass, to determine the density of a metal. This experimental density can then be compared with the density of the metal listed in a reference such as the *Handbook of Chemistry and Physics*. High accuracy means there is good agreement between the experimental value and the known value listed in the reference. Not all measurements can be compared with a known value.

Random and Systematic Errors

The difference between the experimentally measured value of something and the accepted value of something is known as **the error.** For many of the experiments in this course, after you determine the error in your result, you may be required to find the percent error:

$$\text{Percent error} = \frac{\text{theoretical accepted value} - \text{experimentally determined value}}{\text{theoretical accepted value}} \times 100$$

There are two different types of error. **A random error** means that the error has an equal probablilty of being higher or lower than the accepted value. For example, a student measures the density of a quartz sample four times: (Accepted density value for quartz is 2.65 g/mL)

2.72 g/mL	
2.55 g/mL	Since two of the measured density values are below the mean
2.68 g/mL	and two are above the mean, there is an **equal probability** of the
2.60 g/mL	measurements being above or below the mean. This is a **random** error.
	Since the mean density value is very close to the accepted value, the
Mean = 2.64 g/mL	accuracy of the mean measurement is good. (the percent error is 0.38%)

The other type of error is a **systematic error.** This type of error occurs in the same direction each time (either always higher or always lower than the accepted value). For example, a student measures the boiling point of water four times (accepted temperature for the boiling point of water is 100.0° C.)

101.2° C	
100.9° C	Since all four of the measured temperature values are above the accepted
102.0° C	value, the **error** is systematic. The mean value is 1.3% higher than the
101.0° C	accepted value so the accuracy of these measurements is not as good as the
Mean = 101.3° C	accuracy of the density of the measurements in the first example.

Precision and Significant Figures

When a measured value is determined to the highest precision of the measuring instrument, the digits in the measurement are called **significant digits** or **significant figures.**

Suppose we are measuring two pieces of wire, using the metric scale on a ruler that is calibrated in tenths of centimeters as shown in Figures 2.1a and b. One end of the first wire is placed at exactly 0.0 cm and the other end falls somewhere between 6.3 cm and 6.4 cm. Since the distance between 6.3 and 6.4 is very small, it is difficult to determine the next digit exactly. One person might estimate the length of the wire as 6.34 cm and another as 6.33 cm. The estimated digit is never ignored because it tells us that the ruler can be read to the 0.01 place. This measurement therefore has three significant figures (two certain and one uncertain figure).

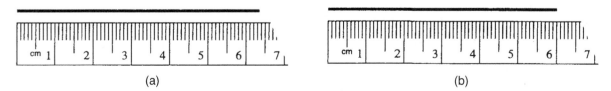

(a)   (b)

Figure 2.1

The second wire has a length which measures exactly 6 cm on the ruler as shown in Figure 2.1b. Reporting this length as 6 cm would be a mistake for it would imply that the 6 is an uncertain digit and others might record 5 or 7 as the measurement. Recording the measurement as 6.0 would also be incorrect because it implies that the 0 is uncertain and that someone else might estimate the length as 6.1 or 5.9. What we really mean is that, as closely as we can read it, the length is exactly 6 cm. So, we must write the number in such a way that it tells how precisely we can read it. In this example we can estimate to 0.01 cm so the length should be reported as 6.00 cm.

Significant Figures in Calculations

The result of multiplication, division, or other mathematical manipulation cannot be more precise than the least precise measurement used in the calculation. For instance, suppose we have an object that weighs 3.62 lb and we want to calculate the mass in grams. $(3.62 \text{ lb})\left(\dfrac{453.6 \text{ g}}{1 \text{ lb}}\right) = 1{,}642.032$ when done by a calculator. To report 1,642.032 g as the mass is absurd, for it implies a precision far beyond that of the original measurement. Although the conversion factor has four significant figures, the mass in pounds has only three significant figures. Therefore the answer should have only three significant figures; that is, 1,640 g. In this case the zero cannot be considered significant. This value can be more properly expressed as 1.64×10^3 g. For a more comprehensive discussion of significant figures see Study Aid 1.

Precise Quantities versus Approximate Quantities

In conducting an experiment it is often unnecessary to measure an exact quantity of material. For instance, the directions might state, "Weigh about 2 g of sodium sulfite." This instruction indicates that the measured quantity of salt should be 2 g plus or minus a small quantity. In this example 1.8 to 2.2 g will satisfy these requirements. To weigh exactly 2.00 g or 2.000 g wastes time since the directions call for approximately 2 g.

Sometimes it is necessary to measure an amount of material precisely within a stated quantity range. Suppose the directions read, "weigh about 2 g of sodium sulfite to the nearest 0.001 g." This instruction does not imply that the amount is 2.000 g but that it should be between 1.8 and 2.2 g and measured and recorded to three decimal places. Therefore, four different students might weigh their samples and obtain 2.141 g, 2.034 g, 1.812 g, and 1.937 g, respectively, and each would have satisfactorily followed the directions.

Temperature

The simple act of measuring a temperature with a thermometer can easily involve errors. Not only does the calibration of the scale on the thermometer limit the precision of the measurement, but the improper placement of the thermometer bulb in the material being measured introduces a common source of human error. When measuring the temperature of a liquid, one can minimize this type of error by observing the following procedures:

1. Hold the thermometer away from the walls of the container.

2. Allow sufficient time for the thermometer to reach equilibrium with the liquid.

3. Be sure the liquid is adequately mixed.

When converting from degrees Celsius to Fahrenheit or vice versa, we make use of the following formulas:

$$°C = \frac{(°F - 32)}{1.8} \text{ or } °F = (1.8 \times °C) + 32$$

Example Problem: Convert 70.0°F to degrees Celsius:

$$°C = \left(\frac{70.0°F - 32}{1.8}\right) = \frac{38.0}{1.8} = 21.11°C \text{ rounded to } 21.1°C$$

This example shows not only how the formula is used but also a typical setup of the way chemistry problems should be written. It shows how the numbers are used, but does not show the multiplication and division, which should be worked out by calculator. The answer was changed from 21.11°C to 21.1°C because the initial temperature, 70.0°F, has only three significant figures. The 1.8 and 32 in the formulas are exact numbers and have no effect on the number of significant figures.

Mass (Weight)

The directions in this manual are written for a 0.001 gram precision balance, but all the experiments can be performed satisfactorily using a 0.01 gram or 0.0001 gram precision balance. Your instructor will give specific directions on how to use the balance, but the following precautions should be observed:

1. The balance should always be "zeroed" before anything is placed on the balance pan. On an electronic digital balance, this is done with the "tare" or "T" button. Balances without this feature should be adjusted by the instructor.

2. Never place chemicals directly on the balance pan; first place them on a weighing paper, weighing "boat", or in a container. Clean up any materials you spill on or around the balance.

3. Before moving objects on and off the pan, be sure the balance is in the "arrest" position. When you leave the balance, return the balance to the "arrest" or standby position.

4. Never try to make adjustments on a balance. If it seems out of order, tell your instructor.

Volume

Beakers and flasks are marked to indicate only approximate volumes. Volume measurements are therefore made in a graduated cylinder by reading the point on the graduated scale that coincides with the bottom of the curved surface called the **meniscus** of the liquid (Figure 2.2). Volumes measured in this illustrated graduated cylinder are calibrated in 1 mL increments and should be estimated and recorded to the nearest 0.1 mL.

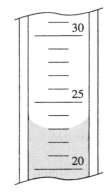

Figure 2.2 Read the bottom of the meniscus. The volume is 23.0 mL

Density

Density is a physical property of a substance and is useful in identifying the substance. **Density** is the ratio of the mass of a substance to the volume occupied by that mass; it is the mass per unit volume and is given by the equations

$$\text{Density} = d = \frac{\text{Mass}}{\text{Volume}} = \frac{m}{V} = \frac{g}{mL} \text{ or } \frac{g}{cm^3}$$

In calculating density it is important to make correct use of units and mathematical setups.

Example Problem: An object weighs 283.5 g and occupies a volume of 14.6 mL. What is its density?

$$d = \frac{m}{V} = \frac{283.5 \text{ g}}{14.6 \text{ mL}} = 19.4 \text{ g/mL}$$

Note that all the operations involved in the calculation are properly indicated and that all units are shown. If we divide grams by milliliters, we get an answer in grams per milliliter.

The volume of an irregularly shaped object is usually measured by the displacement of a liquid. An object completely submerged in a liquid displaces a volume of the liquid equal to the volume of the object.

Measurement data and calculations must always be accompanied by appropriate units.

PROCEDURE

Wear protective glasses.

Record your data on the report form as you complete each measurement, never on a scrap of paper which can be lost or misplaced.

A. Temperature

Record all temperatures to the **nearest 0.1°C.**

1. Fill a 400 mL beaker half full of tap water. Place your thermometer in the beaker. Give it a minute to reach thermal equilibrium. Keeping the thermometer in the water and holding the tip of the thermometer away from the glass, read and record the temperature.

2. Fill a 150 mL beaker half full of tap water. Set up a ring stand with the ring and wire gauze at a height so the hottest part of the burner flame will reach the bottom of the beaker. Heat the water to boiling. Read and record the temperature of the boiling water, being sure to hold the thermometer away from the bottom of the beaker.

3. Fill a 250 mL beaker one-fourth full of tap water and add a 100 mL beaker of crushed ice. Without stirring, place the thermometer in the beaker, resting it on the bottom. Wait at least 1 minute, then read and record the temperature. Now stir the mixture for about 1 minute. If almost all the ice melts, add more. Holding the thermometer off the bottom, read and record the temperature. Save the ice-water mixture for Part 4.

4. Weigh approximately 5 g of sodium chloride and add it to the ice-water mixture. Stir for 1 minute, adding more ice if needed. Read and record the temperature. Dispose of the salt water/ice mixture in the sink.

WASTE
DISPOSE OF
PROPERLY

B. Mass

Using the balance provided, do the following, recording all the masses to include one uncertain digit and all certain digits.

1. Weigh a 250 mL beaker.

2. Weigh a 125 mL Erlenmeyer flask.

3. Weigh a piece of weighing paper or a plastic weighing "boat."

4. Add approximately 2 g of sodium chloride to the weighing paper from step 3 and record the total mass. Calculate the mass of sodium chloride.

C. Length

Using a ruler, make the following measurements in centimeters; measure to the nearest uncertain digit.

1. Measure the length of the arrow on the right ⟶

2. Measure the external height of a 250 mL beaker.

3. Measure the length of a test tube.

D. Volume

Using the graduated cylinder most appropriate, measure the following volumes to the maximum precision possible, usually 0.1 mL. Remember to read the volume at the meniscus.

1. Fill a test tube to the brim with water and measure the volume of the water.

2. Fill a 125 mL Erlenmeyer flask to the brim with water and measure the volume of the water.

3. Measure 5.0 mL of water in a graduated cylinder and pour it into a test tube. With a ruler, measure the height (in cm) and mark the height with a marker.

4. Measure 10.0 mL of water in the graduated cylinder and pour it into a test tube like the one used in the previous step. Again, mark the height with a marker.

In the future, you will often find it convenient to estimate volumes of 5 and 10 mL simply by observing the height of the liquid in the test tube.

E. Density

Estimate and record all volumes to the highest precision, usually 0.1 mL. Make all weighing to the highest precision of the balance. Note that you must supply the units for the measurements and calculations in this section.

1. Density of Water.   Weigh a clean, dry 50 mL graduated cylinder and record its mass. (Graduated cylinders should never be dried over a flame.) Fill the graduated cylinder with distilled water to 50.0 mL. Use a medicine dropper to adjust the meniscus to the 50.0 mL mark. Record the volume. Reweigh and calculate the density of water.

2. Density of a Rubber Stopper.   Select a solid rubber stopper which is small enough to fit inside the 50 mL graduated cylinder. Weigh the dry stopper. Fill the 50 mL cylinder with tap water to approximately 25 mL. Read and record the exact volume. Carefully place the rubber stopper into the graduated cylinder so that it is submerged. Read and record the new volume. Calculate the volume and density of the rubber stopper.

3. Density of a Solid Object.   Obtain a solid object from your instructor. Record the sample code on the report form. Determine the density of your solid by following the procedure given in Part 2 for the rubber stopper. To avoid the possibility of breakage, incline the graduated cylinder at an angle and slide, rather than drop, the solid into it.

Return the solid object to your instructor.

REPORT FOR EXPERIMENT 2

Measurements

A. Temperature

1. Water at room temperature   _____ °C

2. Boiling point   _____ °C

3. Ice water

    Before stirring   _____ °C

    After stirring for 1 minute   _____ °C

4. Ice water with salt added   _____ °C

B. Mass

1. 250 mL beaker   _____ g

2. 125 mL Erlenmeyer flask   _____ g

3. Weighing paper or weighing boat   _____ g

4. Mass of weighing paper/boat + sodium chloride   _____ g

    Mass of sodium chloride (show calculation setup)   _____ g

C. Length

1. Length of ————————————————————▶   _____ cm

2. Height of 250 mL beaker   _____ cm

3. Length of test tube   _____ cm

D. Volume

1. Test tube   _____ mL

2. 125 mL Erlenmeyer flask   _____ mL

3. Height of 5.0 mL of water in test tube   _____ cm

4. Height of 10.0 mL of water in test tube   _____ cm

E. Density

1. Density of Water

Mass of empty graduated cylinder   _____

Volume of water   _____

Mass of graduated cylinder and water   _____

Mass of water (show calculation setup)   _____

Density of water (show calculation setup)   _____

2.   Density of a Rubber Stopper

Mass of rubber stopper   _____

Initial volume of water in cylinder   _____

Final volume of water in cylinder (including stopper)   _____

Volume of rubber stopper (show calculation setup)   _____

Density of rubber stopper (show calculation setup)   _____

3.   Density of a Solid Object

Number of solid object   _____

Mass of solid object   _____

Initial volume of water in graduated cylinder   _____

Final volume in graduated cylinder   _____

Volume of solid object (show calculation setup)   _____

Density of solid object (show calculation setup)   _____

QUESTIONS AND PROBLEMS

1. The directions state "weigh about 5 grams of sodium chloride". Give minimum and maximum amounts of sodium chloride that would satisfy these instructions.

2. Two students each measured the density of a quartz sample three times:

	Student A	*Student B*
1.	3.20 g/mL	2.82 g/mL
2.	2.58 g/mL	2.48 g/mL
3.	2.10 g/mL	2.59 g/mL
mean	2.63 g/mL	2.63 g/mL

   The density found in the *Handbook of Chemistry and Physics* for quartz is 2.65 g/mL

   (a) Which student measured density with the greatest precision? Explain your answer.

   (b) Which student measured density with the greatest accuracy? Explain your answer.

   (c) Are the errors for these students random or systematic? Explain.

Show calculation setups and answers for the following problems.

3. Convert 21°C to degrees Fahrenheit.   _____

4. Convert 101°F to degrees Celsius.   _____

5. An object is 9.6 cm long. What is the length in inches?   _____

6. An empty graduated cylinder weighs 82.450 g. When filled to 50.0 mL with an unknown liquid it weighs 110.810 g. What is the density of the unknown liquid?

_____

7. It is valuable to know that 1 milliliter (mL) equals 1 cubic centimeter (cm^3 or cc). How many cubic centimeters are in an 8.00 oz bottle of cough medicine? (1.00 oz = 29.6 mL)

_____

8. A metal sample weighs 56.8 g. How many ounces does this sample weigh? (1 lb = 16 oz)

_____

9. Convert 15 nm into km.

_____

EXPERIMENT 3

Preparation and Properties of Oxygen

MATERIALS AND EQUIPMENT

Solids: candles, magnesium (Mg) strips, manganese dioxide (MnO_2), fine steel wool (Fe), roll sulfur (S), wood splints. **Solution:** 9 percent hydrogen peroxide (H_2O_2). Deflagration spoon, pneumatic trough, 20 to 25 cm length rubber tubing, 25×200 mm ignition tube, five wide-mouth (gas-collecting) bottles, five glass cover-plates, Büchner funnel, heavy-wall filtering flask with side-arm tubulation, rubber suction tubing, filter paper to fit the Büchner funnel. **Demonstration supplies:** cotton, sodium peroxide (Na_2O_2); steel wool, 25×200 mm test tube; Hoffman electrolysis apparatus.

DISCUSSION

Oxygen is the most abundant and widespread of all the elements in the earth's crust. It occurs both as free oxygen gas and combined in compounds with other elements. Free oxygen gas is diatomic and has the formula O_2. Oxygen is found combined with more elements than any other single element, and it will combine with all the elements except some of the noble gases. Water is 88.9 percent oxygen by mass and the atmosphere is about 21 percent oxygen by volume. Oxygen gas is colorless and odorless, and is only very slightly soluble in water, a property important to its collection in this experiment.

Oxygen may be obtained by decomposing a variety of oxygen-containing compounds. Some of these are mercury(II) oxide (HgO, mercuric oxide), lead(IV) oxide (PbO_2, lead dioxide), potassium chlorate ($KClO_3$), potassium nitrate (KNO_3), hydrogen peroxide (H_2O_2), and water (H_2O).

In this experiment oxygen is produced by decomposing hydrogen peroxide, and five bottles of oxygen will be collected by the downward displacement of water. After collection, some of the physical and chemical properties of oxygen will be observed.

A.   Decomposition of Hydrogen Peroxide to Generate Oxygen

Hydrogen peroxide decomposes very slowly at room temperature. The rate of decomposition is greatly increased by adding a catalyst, manganese dioxide. Although manganese dioxide contains oxygen, it is not decomposed under conditions of this experiment. These equations represent the changes that occur.

$\quad$ **Word Equation:** $\qquad$ Hydrogen peroxide $\longrightarrow$ Water + Oxygen

$\quad$ **Formula Equation:** $\qquad$ $2\,H_2O_2(aq) \xrightarrow{\text{MnO}_2} 2\,H_2O(l) \,+\, O_2(g)$

B.   Collection of Oxygen

The oxygen is collected by a method known as the downward displacement of water. The gas is conducted from a generator to a bottle of water inverted in a pneumatic trough

(Figure 3.1). The oxygen, which is only very slightly soluble in the water, rises in the bottle and pushes the water down and out. Because oxygen is heavier than air, a glass plate is used to cover the opening of the bottle while it is inverted to a right-side-up position and placed on the benchtop until tested.

C. Properties of Oxygen

Like all kinds of matter, oxygen has both physical and chemical properties and you will observe both in this experiment. One outstanding and important chemical property of oxygen is its ability to support combustion. During combustion oxygen is consumed but does not burn and this ability to support combustion is one test for oxygen. Other substances (a wooden splint or a candle, for example) burn in oxygen producing a visible flame and heat. Compounds containing oxygen and one other element are known as **oxides**. Thus when elements such as sulfur, hydrogen, carbon, and magnesium burn in air or oxygen, they form sulfur dioxide, hydrogen oxide (water), carbon dioxide, and magnesium oxide, respectively. These chemical reactions may be represented by equations; for example:

Word Equation: Sulfur + Oxygen $\longrightarrow$ Sulfur dioxide

Formula Equation: $S(s) + O_2(g) \longrightarrow SO_2(g)$

See Study Aid 2 for a discussion of writing formulas and chemical equations.

PROCEDURE

A. and B.   Generation and Collection of Oxygen from Hydrogen Peroxide

Wear protective glasses.
Wash hydrogen peroxide off your skin with water immediately.

1. Assemble the apparatus shown in Figure 3.1. It consists of a 250 mL Erlenmeyer flask, two-hole stopper, thistle tube, glass right-angle bend (Figure 1.3B), glass delivery tube with 135 degree bend (Figure 1.3C), and a 20−25 cm length of rubber tubing. The thistle tube should be at least 24 cm (~10 in.) long and be inserted in the rubber stopper so that there is about 3 mm (1/8 in.) clearance between the end of the tube and the bottom of the flask with the stopper in place. Remember to use glycerol when inserting the glass tubing into the rubber stopper and to hold the glass tubing close to the point of insertion.

2. Fill a pneumatic trough with water until the water level is just above the removable shelf. Attach a piece of rubber tubing to the overflow spigot on the trough and put it in the sink so the water will not spill over the edges of the trough onto the counter. Completely fill five wide-mouth bottles with water. Transfer each bottle to the pneumatic trough by covering its mouth with a glass plate, inverting it, and lowering it into the water. Remove the glass plate below the water level. Place two bottles on the shelf in the trough (over the holes), leaving the other three standing for transfer to the shelf when needed.

3. Using a spatula, put a pea-sized quantity of manganese dioxide (MnO_2) in the generator flask. Replace the stopper, stabilize the flask on the ring stand with a clamp, and make sure that all glass-rubber connections are tight. Add 25 mL of water to the flask through the thistle tube. Make sure that the end of the thistle tube is covered with water (to prevent escape of oxygen gas through the thistle tube).

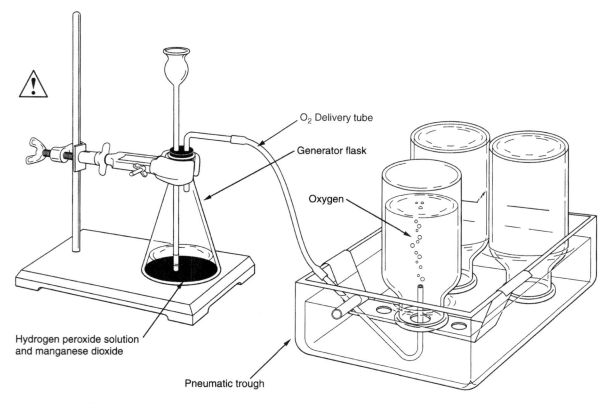

Figure 3.1   Preparing oxygen by decomposing hydrogen peroxide

4. Using a 50 mL graduated cylinder, measure about 50 mL of 9 percent hydrogen peroxide solution.

 Reminder: If hydrogen peroxide gets on your skin, wash it off promptly with water.

To start the generation of oxygen, pour 5 to 10 mL of the peroxide solution into the thistle tube. If all the peroxide solution does not run into the generator, momentarily lift the delivery tube from the water in the trough. Immediately replace the end of the delivery tube under water and into the mouth of the first bottle to collect the gas. When one bottle is filled with gas, immediately start filling the next bottle. Continue generating oxygen by adding an additional 5 to 10 mL portion of hydrogen peroxide whenever the rate of gas production slows down markedly.

5. Cover the mouth of each gas-filled bottle with a glass cover-plate before removing it from the water. Store each bottle mouth upward without removing the glass plate; the oxygen will not readily escape since it is slightly more dense (heavier) than air. **Note which bottle of gas was collected first** and continue until a total of five bottles of gas have been collected.

6. Allow the reaction to go to completion while you continue with the testing of the oxygen you collected. If you have any unreacted H_2O_2 remaining in the graduated cylinder, return it to the special bottle marked "9% unreacted H_2O_2." When you have completed the rest of this experiment, pour the material in the generator into the vacuum flask through the Büchner funnel setup (see Figure 3.2) for waste MnO_2 disposal. Rinse the generator with water. Occasionally the filter paper will need to be changed and the liquid in the filter flask emptied into the sink.

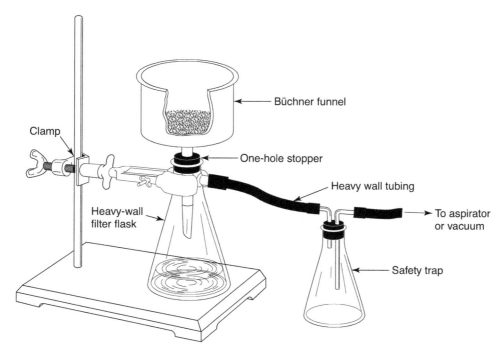

Figure 3.2   Büchner funnel-vacuum flask setup

C.   Properties of Oxygen

Each of the following tests (except C.6) is conducted with a bottle of oxygen and, for comparison, with a bottle of air. Record your observations on the report form.

1. The **glowing splint test** is often used to verify the identity of oxygen. Ignite a wood splint, blow out the flame, and insert the still-glowing splint into the first bottle of oxygen collected. Repeat with a bottle of air. To ensure having a bottle of air, fill the bottle with water and then empty it, thus washing out other gases that may be present.

2. Take a small lump of sulfur in a deflagrating spoon, a bottle of oxygen, and a bottle of air to the fume hood. Light the burner in the fume hood and direct the flame directly into the spoon containing the sulfur. First the sulfur gets dark and melts, then it begins to burn with a blue flame that is barely visible. Lower the burning sulfur alternately into a bottle of oxygen and a bottle of air and compare combustions. Quench the excess burning sulfur in a beaker of water.

3. Stand a small candle (no longer than 5 cm) on a glass plate and light it. Lower a bottle of oxygen over the burning candle, placing the mouth of the bottle on the glass plate. **Measure and record the time,** in seconds, that the candle continues to burn. Repeat with a bottle of air. Note also the difference in the brilliance of the candle flame in oxygen and in air. Return the unused portion of the candle to the reagent shelf.

4. Invert a bottle of oxygen, covered with glass plate, and place it mouth to mouth over a bottle of air. Then remove the glass plate from between the bottles and allow them to stand mouth to mouth for 3 minutes. Cover each bottle with a glass plate and set the bottles down, mouths upward. Test the contents of each bottle by inserting a glowing splint.

5. Pour 25 mL of water into the fifth bottle of oxygen and replace the cover. Place the bottle close to (within 5 or 6 cm) the burner. Take a loose, 4 or 5 cm wad of steel wool (iron) in the crucible tongs and momentarily heat it in the burner flame until some of the steel wool first begins to glow. Immediately lower the glowing metal into the bottle of oxygen. (It is essential that some of the steel wool be glowing when it goes into the oxygen.) Repeat, using a bottle of air.

> **NOTE:** The 25 mL of water is to prevent breakage if the glowing steel wool is accidentally dropped into the bottle.

6. A small strip of magnesium ribbon will be burned next. Read the following precautions before proceeding. *Do not put burning magnesium into a bottle of oxygen.* There is enough oxygen in air for this reaction to proceed vigorously.

 Do not look directly at the burning magnesium ribbon. It is very bright and the light includes considerable ultraviolet light, which can cause damage to the retina of the eye.

Take a 2 to 5 cm strip of magnesium metal in a pair of crucible tongs and ignite it by heating it in the burner flame. After the burning is over, put the product on the Ceramfab plate and compare it to the metal from which it was produced.

D. Instructor Demonstrations (Optional)

1. **Sodium Peroxide as a Source of Oxygen.** Spread some cotton on the bottom of an evaporating dish and sprinkle a small amount (less than 1 g) of fresh sodium peroxide on it. Sprinkle a few drops of water on the peroxide. Spontaneous combustion of the cotton will occur.

2. **Approximate Percentage of Oxygen in the Air.** Push a small wad of steel wool to the bottom of a 25 × 200 mm test tube. Wet the steel wool by covering with water; pour out the surplus water; and place the tube, mouth downward, in a 400 mL beaker half full of water. After the oxygen in the trapped air has reacted with the steel wool—at least three days are needed for complete reaction—adjust the water levels inside and outside the tube to the same height. Cover the mouth of the tube, remove from the beaker, and measure the volume of water in the tube. Alternatively, the height of the water column may be measured (in millimeters) without removing the tube from the beaker. The volume of water in the tube is approximately equal to the volume of oxygen originally present in the tube of air.

$$\% \text{ oxygen} = \left(\frac{\text{Volume of water in tube}}{\text{Volume of tube}} \right)(100)$$

or

$$\% \text{ oxygen} = \left(\frac{\text{Height of water column}}{\text{Length of tube}} \right)(100)$$

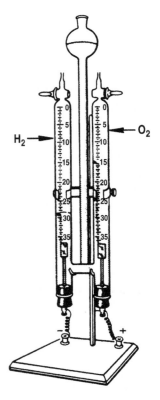

Figure 3.3 Hoffman electrolysis apparatus

3. **Decomposition of Water.** Set up the Hoffman electrolysis apparatus, as shown in Figure 3.3. The solution used in the apparatus should contain about 2 mL of sulfuric acid per 100 mL of water. Direct current may be obtained from several 1.5 volt type A cells connected in series or from some other D.C. source.

NAME _____

SECTION _____ DATE _____

INSTRUCTOR _____

REPORT FOR EXPERIMENT 3

Preparation and Properties of Oxygen

A. and B.   Generation and Collection of Oxygen

1. What evidence did you observe that oxygen is not very soluble in water?

2. What is the source of oxygen in the procedure you used?

   Name _____ Formula _____

3. What purpose does the manganese dioxide serve in this preparation of oxygen?

4. What gas was in the apparatus before you started generating oxygen? Where did it go?

5. What is different about the composition of the first bottle of gas collected compared to the other four?

6. Why are the bottles of oxygen stored with the mouth up?

7. (a) What is the symbol of the element oxygen?   _____

   (b) What is the formula for oxygen gas?   _____

8. Which of the following formulas represent oxides? (Circle) MgO, KClO$_3$, SO$_2$, MnO$_2$,   O$_2$,   NaOH,   PbO$_2$,   Na$_2$O$_2$

9. Write the word and formula equations for the preparation of oxygen from hydrogen peroxide.

   Word Equation:

   Formula Equation:

10. What substances, other than oxygen, are in the generator when the decomposition of H_2O_2 is complete?

C. Properties of Oxygen

1. Write word equations for the chemical reactions that occurred. (See Study Aid 2.)

   C.1. Combustion of wood. Assume carbon is the combustible material.

   C.2. Combustion of sulfur.

   C.5. Combustion of steel wool (iron). (Call the product iron oxide.)

   C.6. Combustion of magnesium.

2. Write formula equations for these four chemical reactions.

   C.1. (CO_2 is the formula for the oxide of carbon that is formed.)

   C.2. (SO_2 is the formula for the oxide of sulfur that is formed.)

C.5. (Fe_3O_4 is the formula for the oxide of iron that is formed.)

C.6. (MgO is the formula for the oxide of magnesium that is formed.)

3. Combustion of a candle.

   (a) Number of seconds that the candle burned in the bottle of oxygen.   _____

   (b) Number of seconds that the candle burned in the bottle of air.   _____

   (c) Explain this difference in combustion time.

   (d) Is it scientifically sound to conclude that all the oxygen in the bottle was reacted when the candle stopped burning? Explain.

4. What were the results of the experiment in which a bottle of oxygen was placed over a bottle of air? Explain the results.

5. (a) Describe the material that is formed when magnesium is burned in air.

   (b) What elements are in this product?

6. (a) What is your conclusion about the rate or speed of a chemical reaction with respect to the concentration of the reactants—for example, a combustion in a high concentration of oxygen (pure oxygen) compared to a combustion in a low concentration of oxygen (air)?

   (b) What evidence did you observe in the burning of sulfur to confirm your conclusion in 6(a)?

EXPERIMENT 6

Freezing Points — Graphing of Data

MATERIALS AND EQUIPMENT

Solids: benzoic acid (C_6H_5COOH) and crushed ice. **Liquid:** glacial acetic acid ($HC_2H_3O_2$). Thermometer, watch or clock with second hand, slotted corks or stoppers.

DISCUSSION

All pure substances, elements and compounds, possess unique physical and chemical properties. Just as one human being can be distinguished from all others by certain characteristics — fingerprints or DNA, for example — it is also possible, through knowledge of its properties, to distinguish any given compound from among the many millions that are known.

A.   Melting and Freezing Points of Pure Substances

The melting point and the boiling point are easily determined physical properties that are very useful in identifying a substance. Consequently, these properties are almost always recorded when a compound is described in the chemical literature (textbooks, handbooks, journal articles, etc.). The freezing and melting of a pure substance occurs at the same temperature, measured when the liquid and solid phases of the substance are in equilibrium. When energy is being removed from a liquid in equilibrium with its solid, the process is called freezing; when energy is being added to a solid in equilibrium with its liquid, the process is called melting.

$$\text{liquid} \underset{\substack{\text{+ energy} \\ \text{(melting)}}}{\overset{\substack{\text{(freezing)} \\ \text{- energy}}}{\rightleftharpoons}} \text{solid}$$

In this experiment, we will determine the freezing point of a pure organic compound, glacial acetic acid ($HC_2H_3O_2$). When the experimental freezing point has been determined, it will be compared with the melting point temperature listed in the *Handbook of Chemistry and Physics.*

When heat is removed from a liquid, the liquid particles lose kinetic energy and move more slowly causing the temperature of the liquid to decrease. Finally enough heat is removed and the particles move so slowly that the liquid becomes a solid, often a crystalline solid. The temperature when this happens (the freezing point) is different for different substances.

The amount of energy removed from a quantity of liquid to freeze it, is equal to the amount of energy added to the same quantity of its solid to melt it. Thus, depending on the direction of energy flow, this equilibrium temperature is called the melting point or the freezing point.

B. Freezing Point of Impure Substances

When a substance (solvent) is uniformly mixed with a small amount of another substance (solute), the freezing point of the resulting solution (an "impure substance") will be lower than that of the pure solvent. For example, the accepted freezing point for pure water is 0.0°C. Solutions of salt in water may freeze at temperatures as low as −21°C depending on the amount of salt added to the water. Antifreeze is added to the water in a car radiator to lower the freezing point of the water.

Melting point/freezing point data are of great value in determining the identity and/or purity of substances, especially in the field of organic chemistry. If a sample of a compound melts or freezes appreciably below the known melting point of the pure substance, we know that the sample contains impurities which have lowered the melting point. If the melting point of an unknown compound agrees with that of a known compound, the identity can often be confirmed by mixing the unknown compound with the known and determining the melting point of the mixture. If the melting point of the mixture is the same as that of the known compound, the compounds are identical. On the other hand, a lower melting point for the mixture indicates that the two compounds are not identical.

C. Supercooling During Freezing

Frequently when a substance is being cooled, the temperature will fall below the true freezing point before crystals begin to form. This phenomenon is known as supercooling because the substance is cooled below its freezing point without forming a solid. Supercooling is more likely to occur if the liquid remains very still and undisturbed as its temperature is lowered. When the system is disturbed in any way, for example, by stirring or jarring, crystallization occurs rapidly throughout the system. As the crystals form, heat is released (called the heat of crystallization) and the temperature rises quickly to the freezing point of the substance. Thus, supercooling does not change the freezing point of the substance.

D. Freezing Point Determinations

You will do three freezing point determinations during this experiment using the setup in Figure 6.1.

Trial 1. Freezing point determination of pure glacial acetic acid WITH STIRRING. This will usually eliminate supercooling.

Trial 2. Freezing point determination of pure glacial acetic acid WITHOUT STIRRING. This should enhance the possibility of supercooling but does not guarantee it.

Trial 3. Freezing point determination of acetic acid (the solvent) after benzoic acid (a solute) has been dissolved in it. This will be done WITHOUT STIRRING to enhance supercooling again.

The time/temperature data will be graphed and the freezing point for each trial read from the graph.

PROCEDURE

Wear protective glasses.

> **NOTES:** Since water and other contaminants will influence the freezing points in this experiment, use only clean, dry equipment.
>
> Read and record all temperatures to the nearest 0.1°C.

A. Freezing Point Determination of Pure Glacial Acetic Acid

Trial 1: With stirring

1. Fasten a utility clamp to the top of a clean, dry test tube. Position this clamp-tube assembly on a ring stand so that the bottom of the tube is about 20 cm above the ring stand base.

2. Obtain a slotted one-hole cork (or stopper) to fit the test tube (see Figure 6.1). Insert a thermometer in the cork and position it in the test tube so that the end of the bulb is about 1.5 cm from the bottom of the test tube. Turn the thermometer so that the temperature scale can be read in the slot.

3. Take your test tube, the cork/thermometer and a graduated cylinder to the fume hood. Measure out 10. mL of glacial acetic acid. Pour it into the test tube and close the test tube with the cork/thermometer. Glacial acetic acid is irritating and harmful if inhaled so keep the test tube stoppered while you work outside the hood at your bench. Rinse the graduated cylinder with water immediately.

4. Reclamp the test tube to your ring stand to minimize the risk of spilling. Make sure the thermometer bulb is covered by the acid and adjust the temperature of the acetic acid to approximately 25°C by warming or cooling the tube in a beaker of water.

5. Fill a 400 mL beaker about three-quarters full of crushed ice; add cold water until the ice is almost covered. Position the beaker of ice and water on the ring stand base under the clamped tube-thermometer assembly.

6. Read the temperature of the acetic acid and record as the 0.0 minute time reading in the Data Table. Now loosen the clamp on the ring stand and observe the second hand of your watch or clock. As the second hand crosses 12, lower the clamped tube-thermometer assembly so that all of the acetic acid in the tube is below the surface of the ice water. Fasten the clamp to hold the tube in this position.

7. Loosen the cork on the tube and stir (during Trial 1 only) the acid with the thermometer, keeping the bulb of the thermometer completely immersed in the acid. Take accurate temperature readings at 30-second intervals as the acid cools. (Zero time was when the second hand crossed 12.) Stop stirring and center the thermometer bulb in the tube as soon as you are sure that crystals are forming in the acid (one to four minutes). Circle the temperature reading when the crystals were first observed.

8. Continue to take temperature readings at 30-second intervals until a total time of 12 minutes has elapsed or until the entire volume of liquid becomes solidified. After that occurs, read the temperature for an additional 2 minutes (4 time intervals) and continue with the next step.

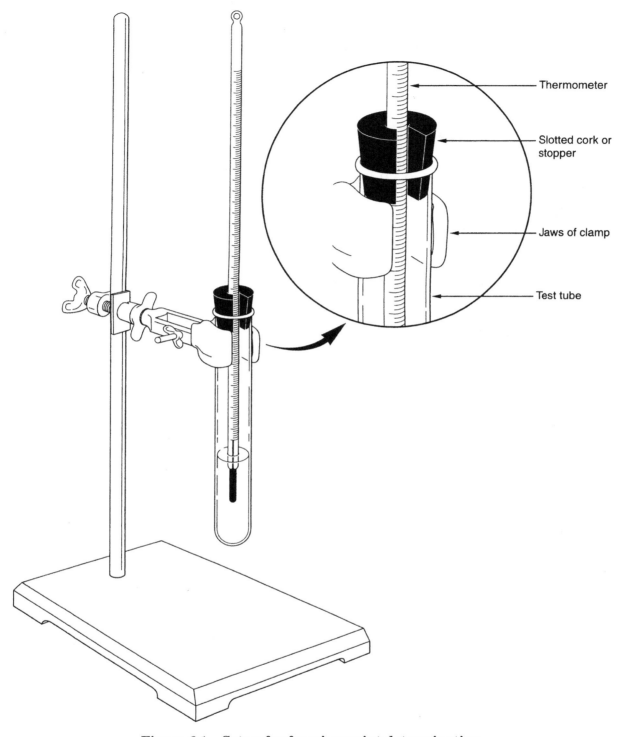

Figure 6.1   Setup for freezing-point determination

9. After completing the temperature readings, remove the test tube-thermometer assembly from the ice bath, keeping the thermometer in place. Immerse the lower portion of the test tube in a beaker of warm water to melt the frozen acetic acid. Do not discard this acid; it will be used in Trials 2 and 3.

Trial 2: Without stirring

10. Repeat steps 4–9 with the following changes:

   a. Replenish the ice bath as in step 5.

   b. After submerging the tube in the ice bath, do NOT stir. Do NOT touch or move the apparatus in any way

   c. If the temperature goes down to about 4°C or lower without the formation of acetic acid crystals and remains there, touch the thermometer and move it until crystals form which usually happens quickly. When you do this be very observant of the temperature changes. Continue to record temperature readings for the full 12 minutes or until the temperature stabilizes after crystallization for 5 minutes.

B. Freezing Point Determination of An Acetic Acid/Benzoic Acid Solution

Trial 3: Without stirring

11. Weigh approximately 0.50 g (between 0.48 and 0.52 g) of benzoic acid crystals. Now remove the thermometer from the test tube of acetic acid and lay it on the table) being careful not to contaminate the thermometer or lose any acid. Carefully add all of the benzoic acid to the acetic acid. Stir gently with the thermometer until all of the crystals have dissolved. Stir for an additional minute or two to ensure a uniform solution. Adjust the temperature of the solution to approximately 25°C.

12. Repeat step 10.

[WASTE DISPOSE OF PROPERLY] 13. Warm the test tube to change the solid to a liquid and dispose of the acetic acid/benzoic acid solution in the waste container provided. Rinse the test tube with water and pour the liquid down the sink.

C. Graphing Temperature Data

Graph the three sets of data using the graph paper in the report form or prepare a computer graph. If necessary, review the instructions for preparing a graph in Study Aid 3.

REPORT FOR EXPERIMENT 6

Freezing Points–Graphing of Data

Data Table

time, minutes	Pure Acetic Acid temp, °C WITH STIRRING	Pure Acetic Acid temp, °C WITHOUT STIRRING	Impure Acetic Acid temp, °C WITHOUT STIRRING
0.0			
0.5			
1.0			
1.5			
2.0			
2.5			
3.0			
3.5			
4.0			
4.5			
5.0			
5.5			
6.0			
6.5			
7.0			
7.5			
8.0			
8.5			
9.0			
9.5			
10.0			
10.5			
11.0			
11.5			
12.0			

Graphing of Freezing Point Data

Plot your data on the graph paper or the computer using a legend as follows:

△ = Pure acetic acid with stirring

▲ = Pure acetic acid without stirring

○ = Acetic acid/benzoic acid solution without stirring

Draw rectangles around the portions of your curves that show supercooling.

QUESTIONS

Use your graph to answer the questions 1–3.

1. a. At what temperature did crystals first form in Trial 1?   _____

   b. Where did the temperature stabilize after supercooling in Trial 2?   _____

   c. What is your experimental freezing point of glacial acetic acid?   _____

   d. What is the theoretical freezing point of glacial acetic acid?   _____
      (Consult the *Handbook of Chemistry and Physics*)

2. How many degrees was the freezing point depressed by the benzoic acid?   _____

   Do this by estimating to the nearest 0.1 degree the number of degrees between the flattest (most nearly horizontal) portions of the curves. Mark the area on the graph with an arrow (↓) to show where this temperature difference estimate was made.

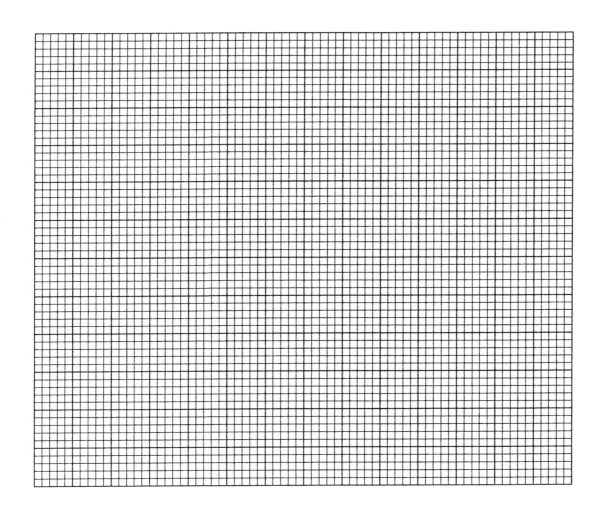

3. a. What is the effect of stirring on the freezing point of pure acetic acid?

    b. What is the effect of stirring on supercooling?

4. a. What do the melting point and freezing point of a substance have in common?

    b. What is the difference between the melting and freezing of a substance?

5. When the solid and liquid phases are in equilibrium, which phase, solid or liquid contains the greater amount of energy? Explain the rationale for your answer.

EXPERIMENT 7

Water in Hydrates

MATERIALS AND EQUIPMENT

Solids: finely ground copper(II) sulfate pentahydrate ($CuSO_4 \cdot 5H_2O$), and unknown hydrate. Cobalt chloride test paper, clay triangle, crucible and cover, 25×200 mm ignition test tube, watch glass.

DISCUSSION

Many salts form compounds in which a definite number of moles of water are combined with each mole of the anhydrous salt. Such compounds are called **hydrates.** The water which is chemically combined in a hydrate is referred to as **water of crystallization** or **water of hydration.** The following are representative examples:

$$CaSO_4 \cdot 2H_2O, \quad CoCl_2 \cdot 6H_2O, \quad MgSO_4 \cdot 7H_2O, \quad Na_2CO_3 \cdot 10H_2O$$

In a hydrate the water molecules are distinct parts of the compound but are joined to it by bonds that are weaker than either those forming the anhydrous salt or those forming the water molecules. In the formula of a hydrate a dot is commonly used to separate the formula of the anhydrous salt from the number of molecules of water of crystallization. For example, the formula of calcium sulfate dihydrate is written $CaSO_4 \cdot 2H_2O$ rather than $CaSO_6H_4$.

Hydrated salts can usually be converted to the anhydrous form by careful heating:

$$\text{Hydrated Salt} \xrightarrow{\Delta} \text{Anhydrous salt} + \text{water}$$

Hydrated salts can be studied qualitatively and quantitatively. In the **qualitative** part of this experiment we will observe some of properties of the liquid (water) driven off by heating the sample. In the **quantitative** part of the experiment we will determine **how much** water was in the hydrate by measuring the amount of water driven off by heating.

To make certain that all of the water in the original sample has been driven off, chemists use a technique known as **heating to constant weight.** Since time expended for this is limited, constant weight is essentially achieved when the sample is heated and weighed in successive heatings until the weight differs by no more than 0.05 g. Thus, if the second weighing is no more than 0.05 g less than the first heating, a third heating is not necessary because the sample has been heated to constant weight (almost). This is a very good reason to follow directions meticulously when heating. If the sample is not heated long enough or at the correct temperature, all of the water may not be driven off completely in the first heating.

Hence it is possible to determine the percentage of water in a hydrated salt by determining the amount of mass lost (water driven off) when a known mass of the hydrate is heated to constant weight.

$$\text{Percentage water} = \left(\frac{\text{Mass lost}}{\text{Mass of sample}} \right) (100)$$

It is possible to condense the vapor driven off the hydrate and demonstrate that it is water by testing it with anhydrous cobalt(II) chloride ($CoCl_2$). Anhydrous cobalt(II) chloride is blue but reacts with water to form the red hexahydrate, $CoCl_2 \cdot 6H_2O$.

PROCEDURE

Wear protective glasses.

A. Qualitative Determination of Water

1. Fold a 2.5 × 20 cm strip of paper lengthwise to form a V-shaped trough or chute. Load about 4 g of finely ground copper(II) sulfate pentahydrate in this trough, spreading it evenly along the length of the trough.

2. Clamp a **dry** 25 × 200 mm ignition test tube so that its mouth is 15–20 degrees **above the horizontal** (Figure 7.1a). Insert the loaded trough into the tube. Rotate the tube to a nearly vertical position (Figure 7.1b) to deposit the copper(II) sulfate in the bottom of the tube. Tap the paper chute gently if necessary, but make sure that no copper sulfate is spilled and adhering to the sides of the upper part of the tube.

3. Remove the chute and turn the tube until it slants mouth downward at an angle of 15–20 degrees **below the horizontal** (Figure 7.1c). Make sure that all of the copper(II) sulfate remains at the bottom of the tube. To obtain a sample of the liquid that will condense in the cooler part of the tube, place a clean, dry test tube, held in an upright position in either a rack or an Erlenmeyer flask, just below the mouth of the tube containing the hydrate.

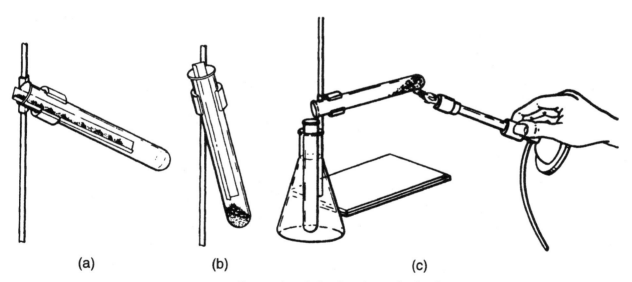

(a)   (b)   (c)

Figure 7.1 Setup for dehydration of a hydrate

4. Heat the hydrate gently at first to avoid excessive spattering. Gradually increase the rate of heating, noting any changes that occur and collecting some of the liquid that condenses in the cooler part of the tube. Continue heating until the blue color of the hydrate has disappeared, but do not heat until the residue in the tube has turned black. Finally warm the tube over its entire length—without directly applying the flame to the clamp—for a minute

or two to drive off most of the liquid that has condensed on the inner wall of the tube. Allow the tube and contents to cool.

NOTE: At excessively high temperatures (above 600°C) copper(II) sulfate decomposes; sulfur trioxide is driven off and the black copper(II) oxide remains as a residue.

Observe and record the appearance and odor of the liquid that has been collected.

5. While the tube is cooling, dry a piece of cobalt chloride test paper by holding it with tongs about 20 to 25 cm above a burner flame; that is, close enough to heat but not close enough to char or ignite the paper. When properly dried, the test paper should be blue. Using a clean stirring rod, place a drop of the liquid collected from the hydrate on the dried cobalt chloride test paper. For comparison place a drop of distilled water on the cobalt chloride paper. Record your observations.

6. Empty the anhydrous salt residue in the tube onto a watch glass and divide it into two portions. Add 3 or 4 drops of the liquid collected from the hydrate to one portion and 3 or 4 drops of distilled water to the other. Compare and record the results of these tests.

 Dispose of solid residues in the waste heavy metal container provided.

B.   Quantitative Determination of Water in a Hydrate

NOTES:

1. **Weigh crucible and contents to the highest precision with the balance available to you.**

2. Since there is some inaccuracy in any balance, use the same balance for successive weighings of the same sample. When subtractions are made to give mass of sample and mass lost, the inaccuracy due to the balance should cancel out.

3. Handle crucibles and covers with tongs only, after initial heating.

4. Be sure crucibles are at or near room temperature when weighed.

5. **Record all data directly on the report form as soon as you obtain them.**

---

1. Obtain a sample of an unknown hydrate, as directed by your instructor. Be sure to record the identifying number.

2. Weigh a clean, dry crucible and cover to the highest precision of the balance.

3. Place between 2 and 3 g of the unknown into the weighed crucible. Cover and weigh the crucible and contents.

4. Place the covered crucible on a clay triangle; adjust the cover so that is slightly ajar, to allow the water vapor to escape (see Figure 7.2); and **very gently** heat the crucible for about 5 minutes. Readjust the flame so that a sharp, inner-blue cone is formed. Heat for another 12 minutes with the tip of the inner-blue cone just touching the bottom of the crucible. The crucible bottom should become dull red during this period.

5. After this first heating is completed, close the cover, cool (about 10 minutes), and weigh.

6. To determine if all the water in the sample was removed during the initial heating, reheat the covered crucible and contents for an additional 6 minutes at maximum temperature; cool and reweigh. If the sample was heated to constant weight the results of the last two weighings should agree within 0.05 g. If the decrease in mass between the two weighings is greater than 0.05 g, repeat the heating and weighing until the results of two successive weighings agree to within 0.05 g.

7. Calculate the percentage of water in your sample on the basis of the *final* weighing.

 Dispose of the solid residue in the waste heavy metal container provided. Return the unused portion of your unknown to the instructor.

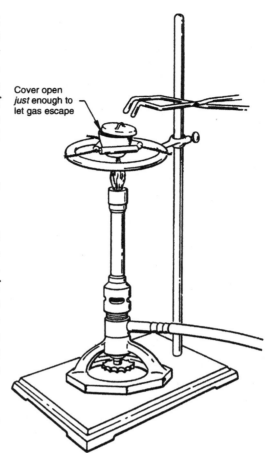

Cover open *just* enough to let gas escape

Figure 7.2   Method of heating a crucible

REPORT FOR EXPERIMENT 7

Water in Hydrates

A. Qualitative Determination of Water

1. Describe the appearance and odor of the liquid obtained by heating copper(II) sulfate pentahydrate.

2. Compare the results observed when testing the liquid from the hydrate and distilled water with the cobalt chloride paper and the anhydrous salt by completing the table below.

Property Observed	Cobalt Chloride Paper	Anhydrous $CuSO_4$
Color before adding liquid(s) to		
Color after adding distilled water to		
Color after adding liquid from hydrate to		
Temperature change after adding distilled water	N/A	
Temperature change after adding liquid from hydrate	N/A	

B. Quantitative Determination of Water in a Hydrate

1. Mass of crucible and cover   _____

2. Mass of crucible, cover, and sample   _____

3. Mass of crucible, cover, and sample after 1st heating   _____

4. Mass of crucible, cover, and sample after 2nd heating _____

5. Mass of crucible, cover, and sample after 3rd heating
   (if needed)   _____

6. Mass of original sample   _____
   Show calculation setup:

7. Total mass lost by sample during heating   _____
   Show calculation setup:

8. Percentage water in sample   Sample No. _____
   Show calculation setup: _____

QUESTIONS AND PROBLEMS

1. What evidence did you see that indicated the liquid obtained from the copper (II) sulfate pentahydrate was water?
   (a)

   (b)

2. What was the evidence of a chemical reaction when the anhydrous salt samples were treated with the liquid obtained from the hydrate and with water?
   (a)

   (b)

3. Write a balanced chemical equation for the decomposition of copper(II) sulfate pentahydrate.

4. When the unknown was heated, could the decrease in mass have been partly due to the loss of some substance other than water? Explain.

5. A student heated a hydrated salt sample with an initial mass of 4.8702 g, After the first heating, the mass had decreased to 3.0662 g.
   (a) If the sample was heated to constant weight after reheating, what is the minimum mass that the sample can have after the second weighing? Show how you determined your answer.

   _____

   (b) The student determined that the mass lost by the sample was 1.8053. What was the percent water in the original hydrated sample? Show calculation setup.

   _____

EXPERIMENT 9

Properties of Solutions

MATERIALS AND EQUIPMENT

Solids: ammonium chloride (NH_4Cl), barium chloride ($BaCl_2$), barium sulfate ($BaSO_4$), fine and coarse crystals of sodium chloride ($NaCl$), and sodium sulfate (Na_2SO_4). **Liquids:** decane ($C_{10}H_{22}$), isopropyl alcohol (C_3H_7OH), and kerosene. **Solutions:** saturated iodine-water (I_2), and saturated potassium chloride (KCl).

DISCUSSION

Solute, Solvent, and Solution

The term **solution** is used in chemistry to describe a homogeneous mixture in which at least one substance (the **solute**) is dissolved in another substance (the **solvent**). The solvent is the substance present in greater quantity and the name of the solution is taken from the name of the solute. Thus, when sodium chloride is dissolved in water, sodium chloride is the solute, water is the solvent, and the solution is called a sodium chloride solution.

In this experiment we will be working with two common types of solutions: those in which a solid solute is dissolved in a liquid solvent (water), and a few in which a liquid solute is dissolved in a liquid solvent.

Like other mixtures, a solution has variable composition, since more or less solute can be dissolved in a given quantity of a solvent. The amount of solute that remains uniformly dispersed throughout the solution after mixing is referred to as the **solution concentration** and can be expressed in many different ways. The maximum concentration that a solution can have varies depending on many factors, including the temperature, the kind of particles in the solute, and interactions between the solute particles and the solvent. In general, water, which is polar, is a better solvent for inorganic than for organic substances. On the other hand, nonpolar solvents such as benzene, decane, and ether are good solvents for many organic substances that are practically insoluble in water.

Dissolved solute particles can be either molecules or ions and their size is of the order of 10^{-8} to 10^{-7} cm (1-10 Å). Many substances will react chemically with each other only when they are dissociated into ions in solution. For example, when the two solids sodium chloride ($NaCl$) and silver nitrate ($AgNO_3$) are mixed, no detectable reaction is observed. However, when aqueous solutions of these salts are mixed, their component ions react immediately to form a white precipitate ($AgCl$).

The rate at which a solute and solvent will form a solution depends on several factors, all of which are related to the amount of contact between the solute particles and the solvent. A solid can dissolve only at the surface that is in contact with the solvent. Any change which increases that contact will increase the rate of solution and vice versa. Thus, the rate of dissolving a solid solute depends on:

1. The particle size of the solute
2. Agitation or stirring of the solution
3. The temperature of the solution
4. The concentration of the solute in solution

Solubility, Miscibility, and Concentration

The term **solubility** refers to the maximum amount of solute that will dissolve in a specified amount of solvent under stated conditions. At a specific temperature, there is a limit to the amount of solute that will dissolve in a given amount of solvent.

Solubility can be expressed in a relative, qualitative way. For example a solute may be very soluble, moderately soluble, slightly soluble, or insoluble in a given solvent at a given temperature. Table 8.1 shows how temperature effects the amount of four different salts that dissolve in 100 g of water.

Table 9.1
Temperature Effect on Solubility of Four Salts in Water, g solute/100 g water

	0°C	10°C	20°C	30°C	40°C	50°C	60°C	70°C	80°C	90°C	100°C
KCl	27.6	31.0	34.0	37.0	40.0	42.6	45.5	48.3	51.1	54.0	55.6
NaCl	35.7	35.8	36.0	36.3	36.6	37.0	37.3	37.8	38.4	39.0	39.8
KBr	53.5	59.5	65.2	70.6	75.5	80.2	85.5	90.0	95.0	99.2	104.0
BaCl$_2$	31.6	33.3	35.7	38.2	40.7	43.6	46.6	49.4	52.6	55.7	58.8

The term **miscibility** describes the solubility of two liquids in each other. When both the solute and solvent are liquids, their solubility in each other is described as miscible (soluble) or immiscible (insoluble). For example, ethyl alcohol and water are miscible; oil and water are immiscible.

The **concentration** of a solution expresses how much solute is dissolved in solution and can be expressed several ways:

1. **Dilute vs. Concentrated:** a dilute solution contains a relatively small amount of solute in a given volume of solution; a concentrated solution contains a relatively large amount of solute per unit volume of solution.

2. **Saturated vs. Unsaturated vs. Supersaturated:**

a. A **saturated** solution contains as much dissolved solute as possible at a given temperature and pressure. The dissolved solute is in equilibrium with undissolved solute. A saturated solution can be dilute or concentrated. The solutions described in Table 8.1 are saturated at each temperature.

Solute (solid) $\rightleftharpoons$ Solute (dissolved)

b. **Unsaturated** solutions contain less solute per unit volume than the corresponding saturated solution. Thus, more solute will dissolve in an unsaturated solution (until saturation is reached).

c. **Supersaturated** solutions contain more dissolved solute than is normally present in the corresponding saturated solution. However, a supersaturated solution is in a very unstable state and will form a saturated solution if disturbed. For example, when a small crystal of the dissolved salt is dropped into a supersaturated solution, crystallization begins at once and salt precipitates until a saturated solution is formed.

3. **Mass-percent Solution** is a quantitative expression of concentration expressed as the percent by mass of the solute in a solution. For example, a 10% sodium hydroxide solution contains 10 g of NaOH in 100 g of solution (10 g NaOH + 90 g H$_2$O); 2 g NaOH in 20 g of solution (2 g NaOH + 18 g H$_2$O). The formula for calculating mass percent is:

$$\text{Mass percent} = \left(\frac{\text{g solute}}{\text{g solute } + \text{ g solvent}}\right)(100)$$

4. **Mass per 100 g solvent** is another quantitative expression of concentration (and the one used in Table 8.1). It is not the same as the Mass percent concentration above because the units are g solute/100 g solvent. Thus, for the 10% NaOH solution described in No. 3, the g NaOH/100 g H$_2$O would be calculated as follows:

$$\left(\frac{10 \text{ g NaOH}}{90 \text{ g H}_2\text{O}}\right)(100) = \frac{11 \text{ g NaOH}}{100 \text{ g H}_2\text{O}}$$

5. **Molarity** is the most common quantitative expression of concentration. Molarity is the number of moles (molar mass) of solute per liter of solution. Thus a solution containing 1 mole of NaOH (40.00 g) per liter is 1 molar (abbreviated 1 M). The concentration of a solution containing 0.5 mole in 500 mL (0.5 L) is also 1 M. The formula for calculating molarity is:

$$\text{Molarity} = \frac{\text{moles of solute}}{\text{liter of solution}} = \frac{\text{moles}}{\text{liter}}$$

PROCEDURE

Wear protective glasses.

A. Concentration of a Saturated Solution

> Use the same balance for all weighings.
> Make all weighings to the highest precision of the balance.

1. Prepare a water bath with a 400 mL beaker half full of tap water and heat to boiling. (See Figure 1.6.)

2. Weigh an empty evaporating dish. Obtain 6 mL of saturated potassium chloride solution and pour it into the dish. Weigh the dish with the solution in it and record these masses on the report form.

3. Place the evaporating dish on the beaker of boiling water and continue to boil until the potassium chloride solution has evaporated almost to dryness (about 25 to 30 minutes), **adding more water to the beaker as needed.**

While the evaporation is proceeding, continue with other parts of the experiment.

---

4. Remove the evaporating dish and beaker from the wire gauze and dry the bottom of the dish with a towel. Put the dish on the wire gauze and heat gently for 1-2 minutes to evaporate the last traces of water. Do not heat too strongly because at high temperatures there is danger of sample loss by spattering.

5. Allow the dish with dry potassium chloride to cool on the Ceramfab pad for 5 to 10 minutes and weigh. To be sure that all the water has evaporated from the potassium chloride, put the dish back on the wire gauze and heat gently again for 1-2 minutes.

6. Allow the dish to cool again on the Ceramfab pad for 5 to 10 minutes and reweigh. The second weighing should be no more than 0.05 g less than the first weighing. Otherwise a third heating and weighng should be done.

 7. Add water to the residue in the dish to redissolve the potassium chloride. Pour the solution into the sink and flush generously with water.

B.   Relative Solubility of a Solute in Two Solvents

1. Add about 2 mL of decane and 5 mL of water to a test tube, stopper it, and shake gently for about 5 seconds. Allow the liquid layers to separate and note which liquid has the greatest density.

2. Now, add 5 mL of saturated iodine-water to the test tube, note the color of each layer, insert the stopper, and shake gently for about 20 seconds. Allow the liquids to separate and again note the color of each layer.

 3. Dispose of the mixture in this test tube in the bottle labeled **Decane Waste.**

C.   Miscibility of Liquids

1. Take three dry test tubes and add liquids to each as follows:

    a. 1 mL kerosene and 1 mL isopropyl alcohol

    b. 1 mL kerosene and 1 mL water

    c. 1 mL water and 1 mL isopropyl alcohol

2. Stopper each tube and mix by shaking for about 5 seconds. Note which pairs are miscible. Dispose of the kerosene mixtures (a and b) in the bottle labeled **Kerosene Waste.** Dispose the contents in test tube (c) in the sink.

D. Effect of Particle Size on Rate of Dissolving

1. Fill a dry test tube to a depth of about 0.5 cm with fine crystals of sodium chloride. Fill another dry tube to the same depth with coarse sodium chloride crystals. Add 10 mL of tap water to each tube and stopper. Shake both tubes at the same time, noting the number of seconds required to dissolve the salt in each tube. (Don't shake the tubes for more than two minutes.)

 2. Dispose of these solutions in the sink.

E. Effect of Temperature on Rate of Dissolving

1. Weigh two 0.5 g samples of fine sodium chloride crystals.

2. Take a 100 mL and a 150 mL beaker and add 50 mL tap water to each. Heat the water in the 150 mL beaker to boiling and allow it to cool for about 1 minute.

3. Add the 0.5 g samples of salt to each beaker and observe the time necessary for the crystals to dissolve in the hot water (do not stir).

4. As soon as the crystals are dissolved in the hot water, take the beaker containing the hot solution in your hand, slowly tilt it back and forth, and observe the layer of denser salt solution on the bottom. Repeat with the cold-water solution.

 5. Dispose of these solutions in the sink.

F. Solubility versus Temperature; Saturated and Unsaturated Solutions

1. Label four weighing boats or papers as follows and weigh the stated amounts onto each one.

   a. 1.0 g NaCl   b. 1.4 g NaCl   c. 1.0 g NH_4Cl d. 1.4 g NH_4Cl

2. Record observations in the table provided on the report form as you proceed through 3-6.

3. Add the 1.0 g samples of NaCl and NH_4Cl to separate tubes labeled A and B as shown. Add 5 mL of distilled water to each, stopper and shake until each salt is dissolved.

4. Now add 1.4 g NaCl to test tube A. Add 1.4 g NH_4Cl to test tube B. Stopper and shake for about 3 minutes. Note whether all of the crystals have dissolved.

5. Place both tubes (unstoppered) into a beaker of boiling water, shake occasionally, and note the results after about 5 minutes.

6. Remove the tubes and cool in running tap water for about 1 minute. Let stand for a few minutes and record what you observe.

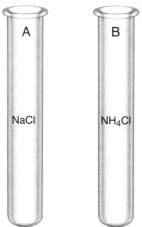

 7. Dispose of these solutions in the sink. Flush generously with water.

G. Ionic Reactions in Solution

1. Into four labeled test tubes, place pea-sized quantities of the following salts, one salt in each tube: (a) barium chloride, (b) sodium sulfate, (c) sodium chloride, (d) barium sulfate.

2. Add 5 mL of water to each tube, stopper, and shake to dissolve. One of the four salts does not dissolve.

3. Mix the barium chloride and sodium sulfate solutions together. Note the results. (Sodium chloride and barium sulfate are the products of this reaction.)

 Dispose of all tubes containing barium in the waste bottle provided. The remaining tubes can be rinsed in the sink.

REPORT FOR EXPERIMENT 9

Properties of Solutions

A. **Concentration of Saturated Solution**

1. Mass of empty evaporating dish   _____

2. Mass of dish + saturated potassium chloride solution   _____

3. Mass of dish + dry potassium chloride, 1st heating   _____

4. Mass of dish + dry potassium chloride, 2nd heating   _____

5. Mass of saturated potassium chloride solution   _____
   Show Calculation Setup

6. Mass of potassium chloride in the saturated solution   _____
   Show Calculation Setup

7. Mass of water in the saturated potassium chloride solution   _____
   Show Calculation Setup

8. Mass percent of potassium chloride in the saturated solution   _____
   Show Calculation Setup

9. Grams of potassium chloride per 100 g of water (experimental)   _____
   in the original solution.
   Show Calculation Setup

10. Grams of potassium chloride per 100 g of water (theoretical)   _____
    (From Table 8.1) at 20°C.

B.   Relative Solubility of a Solute in Two Solvents

1. (a) Which liquid is denser, decane or water?   _____

    (b) What experimental evidence supports your answer?

2. Color of iodine in water: _____

    Color of iodine in decane: _____

3. (a) In which of the two solvents used is iodine more soluble?   _____

    (b) Cite experimental evidence for your answer.

C.   Miscibility of Liquids

1. Which liquid pairs tested are miscible?

2. How do you classify the liquid pair decane—H_2O, miscible or immiscible?

                                                                       _____

D.   Rate of Dissolving Versus Particle Size

1. Time required for fine salt crystals to dissolve   _____

2. Time required for coarse salt crystals to dissolve   _____

3. Since the amount of salt, the volume of water, and the temperature of the systems were identical in both test tubes, how do you explain the difference in time for dissolving the fine vs. the coarse salt crystals?

E.   Rate of Dissolving Versus Temperature

1. Under which condition, hot or cold, did the salt dissolve faster? _____

2. Since the amount of salt, the volume of water, and the texture of the salt crystals were identical in both best tubes, how do you explain the difference in time for dissolving at the hot vs. cold temperatures?

F. Solubility vs. Temperature; Saturated and Unsaturated Solutions

Data Table: Circle the choices which best describe your observations.

	NaCl	**NH₄Cl**
1.0 g + 5 mL water	dissolved completely? yes/no saturated or unsaturated?	dissolved completely? yes/no saturated or unsaturated?
1.0 g + 5 mL water + 1.4 g	dissolved completely? yes/no saturated or unsaturated?	dissolved completely? yes/no saturated or unsaturated?
2.4 g + 5 mL water + heat	dissolved completely? yes/no saturated or unsaturated?	dissolved completely? yes/no saturated or unsaturated?
2.4 g + 5 mL water after cooling	dissolved completely? yes/no saturated or unsaturated?	dissolved completely? yes/no saturated or unsaturated?

G. Ionic Reactions in Solution

1. Write the word and formula equations representing the chemical reaction that occurred between the barium chloride solution, $BaCl_2(aq)$, and the sodium sulfate solution, $Na_2SO_4(aq)$.

   Word Equation:

   Formula Equation:

2. (a) Which of the products is the white precipitate?   _____

   (b) What experimental evidence leads you to this conclusion?

SUPPLEMENTARY QUESTIONS AND PROBLEMS

1. Use the solubility data in Table 9.1 to answer the following:
   Show Calculations

   (a) What is the percentage by mass of NaCl in a saturated solution of sodium chloride at 50°C?

   _____

(b) Calculate the solubility of potassium bromide at 23°C. Hint: Assume that the solubility increases by an equal amount for each degree between 20°C and 30°C.

_____

(c) A saturated solution of barium chloride at 30°C contains 150 g water. How much additional barium chloride can be dissolved by heating this solution to 60°C?

_____

2. A solution of KCl is saturated at 50°C.
Use Table 9.1

(a) How many grams of solute are dissolved in 100 g of water?   _____

(b) What is the total mass of the solution?   _____

(c) What is the mass percent of this solution at 50°C?   _____

(d) If the solution is heated to 100°C, how much more KCl can be dissolved in the solution without adding more water?

_____

(e) If the solution is saturated at 100°C and then cooled to 30°C, how many grams of solute will precipitate out?

_____

EXPERIMENT 10

Composition of Potassium Chlorate

MATERIALS AND EQUIPMENT

Solids: Reagent Grade potassium chlorate ($KClO_3$) and potassium chloride (KCl). **Solutions:** dilute (6 M) nitric acid (HNO_3) and 0.1 M silver nitrate ($AgNO_3$). Two No. 0 crucibles with covers; Ceramfab pad.

DISCUSSION

The **percentage composition** of a compound is the percentage by mass of each element in the compound. If the formula of a compound is known, the percentage composition can be calculated from the molar mass and the total mass of each element in the compound. The **molar mass** of a compound is determined by adding up the atomic masses of all the atoms making up the formula. The **total mass** of an element in a compound is determined by multiplying the atomic mass of that element by the number of atoms of that element in the formula. The percentage of each element is then calculated by dividing its total mass in the compound by the molar mass of the compound and multiplying by 100.

The percentage composition of many compounds may be directly determined or verified by experimental methods. In this experiment the percentage composition of potassium chlorate will be determined both experimentally and from the formula.

When potassium chlorate is heated to high temperatures (above 400°C) it decomposes to potassium chloride and elemental oxygen, according to the following equation:

$$2\,KClO_3(s) \xrightarrow{\Delta} 2\,KCl(s) + 3\,O_2(g)$$

The relative amounts of oxygen and potassium chloride are measured by heating a weighed sample of potassium chlorate until all of the oxygen has been released from the sample. This is accomplished when the sample is heated to constant weight. In this experiment you will heat, cool, and weigh the sample at least twice. If the sample loses more than 0.05 g after the second heating it has not been heated to constant weight and should be heated a third time.

From the experiment we obtain the following three values:

1. Mass of original sample ($KClO_3$).

2. Mass lost when sample was heated (Oxygen).

3. Mass of residue (KCl).

From these experimental values (and a table of atomic masses) we can calculate the following:

4. Percentage oxygen in sample (Experimental value)

$$= \left(\frac{\text{Mass lost by sample}}{\text{Original sample mass}} \right)(100)$$

5. Percentage KCl in sample (Experimental value)

$$= \left(\frac{\text{Mass of residue}}{\text{Original sample mass}}\right)(100)$$

6. Percentage oxygen in $KClO_3$ from formula (Theoretical value)

$$= \left(\frac{3 \text{ at. masses of oxygen}}{\text{Molar mass of } KClO_3}\right)(100) = \left(\frac{3 \times 16.00 \text{ g}}{122.6 \text{ g}}\right)(100)$$

7. Percentage KCl in $KClO_3$ from formula (Theoretical value)

$$= \left(\frac{\text{Molar mass of KCl}}{\text{Molar mass of } KClO_3}\right)(100) = \left(\frac{74.55 \text{ g}}{122.6 \text{ g}}\right)(100)$$

8. Percentage error in experimental oxygen determination

$$= \left(\frac{\text{Theoretical value} - \text{Experimental value}}{\text{Theoretical value}}\right)(100)$$

PROCEDURE

 PRECAUTIONS: Since potassium chlorate is a strong oxidizing agent it may cause fires or explosions if mixed or heated with combustible (oxidizable) materials such as paper. Observe the following safety precautions when working with potassium chlorate:

1 **Wear protective glasses.**

2. Use clean crucibles that have been heated and cooled prior to adding potassium chlorate.

3. Use Reagent Grade potassium chlorate.

 4. **Dispose of any excess or spilled potassium chlorate as directed by your instructor. (Potassium chlorate may start fires if mixed with paper or other solid wastes.)**

5. Heat samples slowly and carefully to avoid spattering molten material—and to avoid poor experimental results.

NOTES:

1. Make all weighings to the highest precision possible with the balance available to you. Use the same balance to make all weighings for a given sample. Record all data directly on the report sheet as they are obtained.

2. Duplicate samples of potassium chlorate are to be analyzed, if two crucibles are available.

3. For utmost precision, handle crucibles with tongs after the initial heating.

A. Determining Percentage Composition

Place a clean, dry crucible (uncovered) on a clay triangle and heat for 2 or 3 minutes at the maximum flame temperature. The tip of the sharply defined inner-blue cone of the flame should almost touch and heat the crucible bottom to redness. Allow the crucible to cool. If two crucibles are being used, carefully transfer the first to a Ceramfab pad and heat the second while the first crucible is cooling.

Weigh the cooled crucible and its cover; add between 1 and 1.5 g of potassium chlorate; weigh again.

> **NOTE:** The crucible must be covered when potassium chlorate is being heated in it.

Place the covered crucible on the clay triangle and **heat gently for 8 minutes** with the tip of the inner-blue cone of the flame 6 to 8 cm (about 2.5 to 3 in.) below the crucible bottom. Then carefully lower the crucible or raise the burner until the tip of the sharply defined inner-blue cone just touches the bottom of the crucible, and heat for an additional 10 minutes. The bottom of the crucible should be heated to a dull red color during this period.

Grasp the crucible just below the cover with the concave part of the tongs and very carefully transfer it to a Ceramfab pad. Allow to cool (about 10 minutes) and weigh. Begin analysis of a second sample while the first is cooling.

After weighing, reheat the first sample for an additional 6 minutes at the maximum flame temperature (bottom of the crucible heated to a dull red color); cool and reweigh. If the residue is at constant weight, the last two weighings should be in agreement. If the mass decreased more than 0.05 g between these two weighings, repeat the heating and weighing until two successive weighings agree within 0.05 g. Use the final weight in your calculations.

Complete the analysis of the second sample following the same procedure used for the first.

B. Qualitative Examination of Residue

This part of the experiment should be started as soon as the final heating and weighing of the first sample is completed and while the second sample is in progress.

Number and place three clean test tubes in a rack. Put a pea-sized quantity of potassium chloride into tube No. 1 and a like amount of potassium chlorate into tube No. 2. Add 10 mL of distilled water to each of these two tubes and shake to dissolve the salts. Now add distilled water to the crucible containing the residue from the first sample so it is one-half full. Heat the uncovered crucible very gently for about 1 minute; transfer 1 to 2 mL of the resulting solution from the crucible to tube No. 3; add about 10 mL of distilled water and mix.

Test the solution in each tube as follows: Add 5 drops of dilute (6 M) nitric acid and 5 drops of 0.1 M silver nitrate solution. Mix thoroughly. Record your observations. This procedure using nitric acid and silver nitrate is a general test for chloride ions. The formation of a white precipitation is a positive test and indicates the presence of chloride ions. A positive test is obtained with any substance that produces chloride ions in solution.

 Dispose of solutions and precipitates containing silver in the heavy metal waste container provided. Dispose of the remaining contents in the crucible down the sink.

REPORT FOR EXPERIMENT 10 INSTRUCTOR _____

Composition of Potassium Chlorate

A. Determining Percentage Composition	**Sample 1**	**Sample 2**
1. Mass of crucible + cover	_____	_____
2. Mass of crucible + cover + sample before heating	_____	_____
3. Mass of crucible + cover + residue after 1st heating	_____	_____
4. Mass of crucible + cover + residue after 2nd heating	_____	_____
5. Mass of crucible + cover + residue after 3rd heating (if necessary)	_____	_____
6. Mass of original sample Show sample 1 calculation setup:	_____	_____
7. Mass lost (total) during heating Show sample 1 calculation setup:	_____	_____
8. Final mass of residue Show sample 1 calculation setup:	_____	_____
9. Experimental percent oxygen in sample ($KClO_3$) Show sample 1 calculation setup:	_____	_____
10. Experimental percent KCl in sample ($KClO_3$) Show sample 1 calculation setup:	_____	_____
11. Theoretical percent oxygen in $KClO_3$ Show calculation setup:	_____	
12. Theoretical percent KCl in $KClO_3$ Show calculation setup	_____	
13. Percent error in experimental % oxygen determination Show sample 1 calculation setup	_____	_____

B.   Qualitative Examination of Residue

1. Record what you observed when silver nitrate was added to the following:

    (a) Potassium chloride solution

    (b) Potassium chlorate solution

    (c) Residue solution

2. (a) What evidence did you observe that would lead you to believe that the residue was potassium chloride?

    (b) What would happen if you added silver nitrate to a solution of sodium chloride? Explain your answer.

    (c) Did the evidence obtained in the silver nitrate tests of the three solutions prove conclusively that the residue actually was potassium chloride? Explain?

QUESTIONS AND PROBLEMS

1. A student forgot to read the label on the jar carefully and put potassium chloride in the crucible instead of potassium chlorate. How would the results turn out?

2. What if a potassium chlorate sample is contaminated with KCl. Would the experimental % oxygen be higher or lower than the theoretical % oxygen? Explain your answer.

3. What if a potassium chlorate sample is contaminated with moisture. Would an analysis show the experimental % oxygen higher or lower than the theoretical % oxygen? Explain your answer?

4. Calculate the percentage of Cl in $Al(ClO_3)_3$ _____

5. Other metal chlorates when heated show behavior similar to that of potassium chlorate yielding metal chlorides and oxygen. Write the balanced formula equation for the reaction to be expected when calcium chlorate, $Ca(ClO_3)_2$ is heated.

EXPERIMENT 11

Double Displacement Reactions

MATERIALS AND EQUIPMENT

Solid: sodium sulfite (Na_2SO_3). **Solutions:** dilute (6 M) ammonium hydroxide (NH_4OH), 0.1 M ammonium chloride (NH_4Cl), 0.1 M barium chloride ($BaCl_2$), 0.1 M calcium chloride ($CaCl_2$), 0.1 M copper(II) sulfate ($CuSO_4$), dilute (6 M) hydrochloric acid (HCl), concentrated (12 M) hydrochloric acid (HCl), 0.1 M iron(III) chloride ($FeCl_3$), dilute (6 M) nitric acid (HNO_3), 0.1 M potassium nitrate (KNO_3), 0.1 M silver nitrate ($AgNO_3$), 0.1 M sodium carbonate (Na_2CO_3), 0.1 M sodium chloride (NaCl), 10 percent sodium hydroxide (NaOH), dilute (3 M) sulfuric acid (H_2SO_4), and 0.1 M zinc nitrate [$Zn(NO_3)_2$]. Medicine dropper.

DISCUSSION

Double displacement reactions are among the most common of the simple chemical reactions and are comparatively easy to study.

In each part of this experiment two aqueous solutions, each containing positive and negative ions, will be mixed in a test tube. Consider the hypothetical reaction.

$$AB + CD \longrightarrow AD + CB$$

where AB(aq) exists as A^+ and B^- ions in solution and CD(aq) exists as C^+ and D^- ions in solution. As the ions come in contact with each other, there are six possible combinations that might conceivably cause chemical reaction. Two of these combinations are the meeting of ions of like charge; that is, $A^+ + C^+$ and $B^- + D^-$. But since like charges repel, no reaction will occur. Two other possible combinations are those of the original two compounds; that is, $A^+ + B^-$ and $C^+ + D^-$. Since we originally had a solution containing each of these pairs of ions, they can mutually exist in the same solution; therefore they do not recombine. Thus the two possibilities for chemical reaction are the combination of each of the positive ions with the negative ion of the other compound; that is, $A^+ + D^-$ and $C^+ + B^-$. Let us look at some examples.

Example 1. When solutions of sodium chloride and potassium nitrate are mixed, the equation for the double displacement reaction (hypothetical) is

$$NaCl(aq) + KNO_3(aq) \longrightarrow KCl(aq) + NaNO_3(aq)$$

We get the hypothetical products by simply combining each positive ion with the other negative ion. But has there been a reaction? When we do the experiment, we see no evidence of reaction. There is no precipitate formed, no gas evolved, and no obvious temperature change. Thus we must conclude that no reaction occurred. Both hypothetical products are soluble salts, so the ions are still present in solution. We can say that we simply have a solution of four kinds of ions, Na^+, Cl^-, K^+, and NO_3^-.

The situation is best expressed by changing the equation to

$$NaCl(aq) + KNO_3(aq) \longrightarrow No\ reaction$$

Example 2. When solutions of sodium chloride and silver nitrate are mixed, the equation for the double displacement reaction (hypothetical) is

$$NaCl + AgNO_3 \longrightarrow NaNO_3 + AgCl$$

A white precipitate is produced when these solutions are mixed. This precipitate is definite evidence of a chemical reaction. One of the two products, sodium nitrate ($NaNO_3$) or silver chloride ($AgCl$), is insoluble. Although the precipitate can be identified by further chemical testing, we can instead look at the **Solubility Table in Appendix 5** to find that sodium nitrate is soluble but silver chloride is insoluble. We may then conclude that the precipitate is silver chloride and indicate this in the equation with an (s). Thus

$$NaCl(aq) + AgNO_3(aq) \longrightarrow NaNO_3(aq) + AgCl(s)$$

Example 3. When solutions of sodium carbonate and hydrochloric acid are mixed, the equation for the double displacement reaction (hypothetical) is

$$Na_2CO_3(aq) + 2\,HCl(aq) \longrightarrow 2\,NaCl(aq) + H_2CO_3(aq)$$

Bubbles of a colorless gas are evolved when these solutions are mixed. Although this gas is evidence of a chemical reaction, neither of the indicated products is a gas. But carbonic acid, H_2CO_3, is an unstable compound and readily decomposes into carbon dioxide and water.

$$H_2CO_3(aq) \longrightarrow H_2O(l) + CO_2(g)$$

Therefore, CO_2 and H_2O are the products that should be written in the equation. The original equation then becomes

$$Na_2CO_3(aq) + 2\,HCl(aq) \longrightarrow 2\,NaCl(aq) + H_2O(l) + CO_2(g)$$

The evolution of a gas is indicated by a (g).

Examples of some other substances that decompose to form gases are sulfurous acid (H_2SO_3) and ammonium hydroxide (NH_4OH):

$$H_2SO_3(aq) \longrightarrow H_2O(l) + SO_2(g)$$
$$NH_4OH(aq) \longrightarrow H_2O(l) + NH_3(g)$$

Example 4. When solutions of sodium hydroxide and hydrochloric acid are mixed, the equation for the double displacement reaction (hypothetical) is

$$NaOH(aq) + HCl(aq) \longrightarrow NaCl(aq) + H_2O(l)$$

The mixture of these solutions produces no visible evidence of reaction, but on touching the test tube we notice that it feels warm. The evolution of heat is evidence of a chemical reaction. **Example 4** and **Example 1** appear similar because there is no visible evidence of reaction. However, the difference is very important. In **Example 1** all four ions are still uncombined. In **Example 4** the hydrogen ions (H^+) and hydroxide ions (OH^-) are no longer free in solution but have combined to form water. The reaction of H^+ (an acid) and OH^- (a base) is called **neutralization.** The formation of the slightly ionized compound (water) caused the reaction to occur and was the source of the heat liberated.

Water is the most common slightly ionized substance formed in double displacement reactions; other examples are acetic acid ($HC_2H_3O_2$), oxalic acid ($H_2C_2O_4$), and phosphoric acid (H_3PO_4).

From the four examples cited we see that a double displacement reaction will occur if at least one of the following classes of substances is formed by the reaction:

1. A precipitate

2. A gas

3. A slightly ionized compound, usually water

PROCEDURE

Wear protective glasses.

Each part of the experiment (except No. 12) consists of mixing equal volumes of two solutions in a test tube. Use about a **3 mL sample** of each solution (about 1.5 cm of liquid in a standard test tube). It is not necessary to measure each volume accurately. Record your observations at the time of mixing. Where there is no visible evidence of reaction, feel each tube, or check with a thermometer, to determine if heat is evolved (exothermic reaction). In each case where a reaction has occurred, complete and balance the equation, properly indicating precipitates and gases. When there is no evidence of reaction, write the words "No reaction" as the right-hand side of the equation.

1. Mix 0.1 M sodium chloride and 0.1 M potassium nitrate solutions.

2. Mix 0.1 M sodium chloride and 0.1 M silver nitrate solutions.

3. Mix 0.1 M sodium carbonate and **dilute** (6 M) hydrochloric acid solutions.

4. Mix 10 percent sodium hydroxide and dil. (6 M) hydrochloric acid solutions.

5. Mix 0.1 M barium chloride and dil. (3 M) sulfuric acid solutions.

 6. Mix **dilute** (6 M) ammonium hydroxide and **dilute** (3 M) sulfuric acid solutions.

7. Mix 0.1 M copper(II) sulfate and 0.1 M zinc nitrate solutions.

8. Mix 0.1 M sodium carbonate and 0.1 M calcium chloride solutions.

9. Mix 0.1 M copper(II) sulfate and 0.1 M ammonium chloride solutions.

10. Mix 10 percent sodium hydroxide and dil. (6 M) nitric acid solutions.

11. Mix 0.1 M iron(III) chloride and dil. (6 M) ammonium hydroxide solutions.

 12. **Do this part in the fume hood.** Add 1 g of solid sodium sulfite to 3 mL of water and shake to dissolve. Now add about 1 mL of conc. (12 M) hydrochloric acid solution, a drop at a time, using a medicine dropper. Observe the results carefully.

 Dispose of mixtures from reactions 2, 5, 7, 9 in the "heavy metal waste" container. Dispose of the contents of reaction 12 in the sink inside the hood. Dispose of the contents of all other tubes in the sink and flush with water.

REPORT FOR EXPERIMENT 11

Double Displacement Reactions

Directions for completing table below:

1. Record your observations (Evidence of Reaction) of each experiment. Use the following terminology: (a) "Precipitate formed" (include the color), (b) "Gas evolved," (c) "Heat evolved," or (d) "No reaction observed."

2. Complete and balance the equation for each case in which a reaction occurred. First write the correct formulas for the products, taking into account the charges (oxidation numbers) of the ions involved. Then balance the equation by placing a whole number in front of each formula (as needed) to adjust the number of atoms of each element so that they are the same on both sides of the equation. Use (g) or (s) to indicate gases and precipitates. Where no evidence of reaction was observed, write the words "No reaction" as the right-hand side of the equation.

Evidence of Reactions	Balanced Equations
1.	$NaCl \ + \ KNO_3 \longrightarrow$
2.	$NaCl \ + \ AgNO_3 \longrightarrow$
3.	$Na_2CO_3 + \ HCl \longrightarrow$
4.	$NaOH \ + \ HCl \longrightarrow$
5.	$BaCl_2 \ + \ H_2SO_4 \longrightarrow$
6.	$NH_4OH + \ H_2SO_4 \longrightarrow$
7.	$CuSO_4 \ + \ Zn(NO_3)_2 \longrightarrow$
8.	$Na_2CO_3 + \ CaCl_2 \longrightarrow$
9.	$CuSO_4 \ + \ NH_4Cl \longrightarrow$
10.	$NaOH \ + \ HNO_3 \longrightarrow$
11.	$FeCl_3 \ + \ NH_4OH \longrightarrow$
12.	$Na_2SO_3 + \ HCl \longrightarrow$

QUESTIONS AND PROBLEMS

1. The formation of what three classes of substances caused double displacement reactions to occur in this experiment?

    (a)

    (b)

    (c)

2. Write the equation for the decomposition of sulfurous acid.

3. Using three criteria for double displacement reactions, together with the Solubility Table in Appendix 5, predict whether a double displacement reaction will occur in each example below. If reaction will occur, complete and balance the equation, properly indicating gases and precipitates. If you believe no reaction will occur, write "no reaction" as the right-hand side of the equation. All reactants are in aqueous solution.

    (a) $K_2S + CuSO_4 \longrightarrow$

    (b) $NH_4OH + H_2C_2O_4 \longrightarrow$

    (c) $KOH + NH_4Cl \overset{\Delta}{\longrightarrow}$

    (d) $NaC_2H_3O_2 + HCl \longrightarrow$

    (e) $Na_2CrO_4 + Pb(C_2H_3O_2)_2 \longrightarrow$

    (f) $(NH_4)_2SO_4 + NaCl \longrightarrow$

    (g) $BiCl_3 + NaOH \longrightarrow$

    (h) $KC_2H_3O_2 + CoSO_4 \longrightarrow$

    (i) $Na_2CO_3 + HNO_3 \longrightarrow$

    (j) $ZnBr_2 + K_3PO_4 \longrightarrow$

EXPERIMENT 12

Single Displacement Reactions

MATERIALS AND EQUIPMENT

Solids: strips of sheet copper, lead, and zinc measuring about 1×2 cm; and sandpaper or emery cloth. **Solutions:** 0.1 M copper(II) nitrate [$Cu(NO_3)_2$], 0.1 M lead(II) nitrate [$Pb(NO_3)_2$], 0.1 M magnesium sulfate ($MgSO_4$), 0.1 M silver nitrate ($AgNO_3$), and dilute (3 M) sulfuric acid (H_2SO_4). Small test tubes.

DISCUSSION

The chemical reactivity of elements varies over an immense range. Some, like sodium and fluorine, are so reactive that they are never found in the free or uncombined state in nature. Others, like xenon and platinum, are nearly inert and can be made to react with other elements only under special conditions.

The **reactivity** of an element is related to its tendency to lose or gain electrons; that is, to be oxidized or reduced. In principle it is possible to arrange nearly all the elements into a single series in order of their reactivities. A series of this kind indicates which free elements are capable of displacing other elements from their compounds. Such a list is known as an **activity** or **electromotive series.** To illustrate the preparation of an activity series, we will experiment with a small group of selected elements and their compounds.

A generalized single displacement reaction is represented by the equation

$$A(s) + BC(aq) \longrightarrow B(s) + AC(aq)$$

Element A is the more active element and replaces element B from the compound BC. But if element B is more active than element A, no reaction will occur.

Let us consider two specific examples, using copper and mercury.

Example 1. A few drops of mercury metal are added to a solution of copper(II) chloride ($CuCl_2$).

Example 2. A strip of metallic copper is immersed in a solution of mercury(II) chloride ($HgCl_2$).

In Example 1 no change is observed even after the solution has been standing for a prolonged time, and we conclude that there is no reaction. In Example 2 the copper strip is soon coated with metallic mercury, and the solution becomes pale green. From this evidence we conclude that mercury will not displace copper in copper compounds but copper will displace mercury in mercury compounds. Therefore copper is a more reactive metal than mercury and is above mercury in the activity series. In terms of chemical equations these facts may be represented as

Example 1. $Hg(l) + CuCl_2(aq) \longrightarrow$ No reaction

Example 2. $Cu(s) + HgCl_2(aq) \longrightarrow Hg(l) + CuCl_2(aq)$

The second equation shows that, in terms of oxidation numbers (or charges), the chloride ion remained unchanged, mercury changed from +2 to 0, and copper changed from 0 to +2. The +2 oxidation state of copper is the one normally formed in solution.

Expressed another way, the actual reaction that occurred was the displacement of a mercury ion by a copper atom. This can be expressed more simply in equation form:

$$Cu^0(s) + Hg^{2+}(aq) \longrightarrow Hg^0 + Cu^{2+}(aq)$$

In contrast to double displacement reactions, single displacement reactions involve changes in oxidation numbers and therefore are also classified as **oxidation-reduction reactions.**

PROCEDURE

Wear protective glasses.

1. Place six clean small test tubes in a rack and number them 1–6. To each, add about 2 mL of the solutions listed below.

2. Obtain three pieces of sheet zinc, two of copper, and one of lead. Be sure metal strips are small enough to fit into the test tubes. Clean the metal pieces with fine sandpaper or emery cloth to expose fresh metal surfaces. Add the metals to the test tubes with the solutions as listed.

Tube 1: silver nitrate + copper strip
Tube 2: copper(II) nitrate + lead strip
Tube 3: lead(II) nitrate + zinc strip
Tube 4: magnesium sulfate + zinc strip
Tube 5: dilute (3M) sulfuric acid + copper strip
Tube 6: dilute (3M) sulfuric acid + zinc strip

3. Observe the contents of each tube carefully and record any evidence of chemical reaction.

Evidence of reaction will be either evolution of a gas (bubbles) or appearance of a metallic deposit on the surface of the metal strip. Metals deposited from a solution are often black or gray (in the case of copper, very dark reddish brown) and bear little resemblance to commercially prepared metals.

With some of the combinations used in these experiments, the reactions may be slow or difficult to detect. If you see no immediate evidence of reaction, set the tube aside and allow it to stand for about 10 minutes, then reexamine it.

4. Pour the solutions in each test tube into the "heavy metals waste" container. Rinse the metals in tap water and dispose of the strips in the trash. Do not allow the metal strips to go into the sink or into the waste bottle.

REPORT FOR EXPERIMENT 12

Single Displacement Reactions

Evidence of Reaction	Equations (to be completed)
Describe any evidence of reaction; if no reaction was observed, write "None".	Write "No reaction", if no reaction was observed.
1.	$Cu + AgNO_3(aq) \longrightarrow$
2.	$Pb + Cu(NO_3)_2(aq) \longrightarrow$
3.	$Zn + Pb(NO_3)_2(aq) \longrightarrow$
4.	$Zn + MgSO_4(aq) \longrightarrow$
5.	$Cu + H_2SO_4(aq) \longrightarrow$
6.	$Zn + H_2SO_4(aq) \longrightarrow$

QUESTIONS AND PROBLEMS

1. Complete the following table by writing the symbols of the two elements whose reactivities are being compared in each test:

	Tube Number					
	1	2	3	4	5	6
Greater activity						
Lesser activity						

2. Arrange Pb, Mg, and Zn in order of their activities, listing the most active first.

(1) _____

(2) _____

(3) _____

3. Arrange Cu, Ag, and Zn in order of their activities, listing the most active first.

           (1) _____

           (2) _____

           (3) _____

4. Arrange Mg, H, and Ag in order of their activities, listing the most active first.

           (1) _____

           (2) _____

           (3) _____

5. Arrange all five of the metals (excluding hydrogen) in an activity series, listing the most active first.

           (1) _____

           (2) _____

           (3) _____

           (4) _____

           (5) _____

6. On the basis of the reactions observed in the six test tubes, explain why the position of hydrogen cannot be fixed exactly with respect to all of the other elements listed in the activity series in Question 5.

7. What additional test(s) would be needed to establish the exact position of hydrogen in the activity series of the elements listed in Question 5?

8. On the basis of the evidence developed in this experiment:

  (a) Would silver react with dilute sulfuric acid? Why or why not?

  (b) Would magnesium react with dilute sulfuric acid? Why or why not?

EXPERIMENT 14

Identification of Selected Anions

MATERIALS AND EQUIPMENT

Liquids: Decane ($C_{10}H_{22}$). **Solutions:** 0.1 M barium chloride ($BaCl_2$), freshly prepared chlorine water (Cl_2), dilute (6 M) hydrochloric acid (HCl), dilute (6 M) nitric acid (HNO_3), 0.1 M silver nitrate ($AgNO_3$), 0.1 M sodium bromide (NaBr), 0.1 M sodium carbonate (Na_2CO_3), 0.1 M sodium chloride (NaCl), 0.1 M sodium iodide (NaI), 0.1 M sodium phosphate (Na_3PO_4), 0.1 M sodium sulfate (Na_2SO_4), and unknown solutions. Wash bottle for distilled water.

DISCUSSION

The examination of a sample of inorganic material to identify the ions that are present is called **qualitative analysis.** To introduce qualitative analysis, we will analyze for six anions (negatively charged ions). The ions selected for identification are chloride (Cl^-), bromide (Br^-), iodide (I^-), sulfate (SO_4^{2-}), phosphate (PO_4^{3-}) and carbonate (CO_3^{2-}).

Qualitative analysis is based on the fact that no two ions behave identically in all of their chemical reactions. Identification depends on appropriate chemical tests coupled with careful observation of such characteristics as solution color, formation and color of precipitates, evolution of gases, etc. Test reactions are selected to identify the ions in the fewest steps possible. In this experiment only one anion is assumed to be present in each sample. If two or more anions must be detected in a single solution, the scheme of analysis can be considerably more complex.

Silver Nitrate Test

When solutions of the sodium salts of the six anions are reacted with silver nitrate solution, the following precipitates are formed: AgCl, AgBr, AgI, Ag_3PO_4, and Ag_2CO_3. Ag_2SO_4 is moderately soluble and does not precipitate at the concentrations used in these solutions. When dilute nitric acid is added, the precipitates Ag_3PO_4, and Ag_2CO_3 dissolve; AgCl, AgBr, and AgI remain undissolved. Acids react with carbonates to form CO_2 (g). Look for gas bubbles when nitric acid is added to the silver precipitates.

In some cases a tentative identification of an anion may be made from the silver nitrate test. This identification is based on the color of the precipitate and on whether or not the precipitate is soluble in nitric acid. However, since two or more anions may give similar results, second or third confirmatory tests are necessary for positive identification.

Barium Chloride Test

When barium chloride solution is added to solutions of the sodium salts of the six anions, precipitates of $BaSO_4$, $Ba_3(PO_4)_2$ and $BaCO_3$, are obtained. No precipitate is obtained with Cl^-, Br^-, or I^-.

When dilute hydrochloric acid is added, the precipitates $Ba_3(PO_4)_2$ and $BaCO_3$ dissolve; $BaSO_4$ does not dissolve. Look for CO_2 gas bubbles.

Organic Solvent Test

The silver nitrate test can prove the presence of a halide ion (Cl^-, Br^-, or I^-) because the silver precipitates of the other three anions dissolve in nitric acid. But the colors of the three silver halides do not differ sufficiently to establish which halide ion is present.

Adding chlorine water (Cl_2 dissolved in water) to halide salts in solution will oxidize bromide ion to free bromine (Br_2) and iodine ion to free iodine (I_2). The free halogen may be extracted from the water solution by adding an immiscible organic solvent such as decane and shaking vigorously. The colors of the three halogens in organic solvents are quite different. Cl_2 is pale yellow, Br_2 is yellow-orange to reddish-brown, and I_2 is pink to violet. After adding chlorine water and shaking, a yellow-orange to reddish-brown color in the decane layer indicates that Br^- was present in the original solution; a pink to violet color in the decane layer indicates that I^- was present. However, a pale yellow color does not indicate Cl^-, since Cl_2 was added as a reagent. But if the silver nitrate test gives a white precipitate that is insoluble in nitric acid, and the organic solvent test shows no Br^- or I^-, then you can conclude that Cl^- was present.

Though we have described many of the expected results of these tests, it is necessary to test known solutions to actually see the results of the tests and to develop satisfactory experimental techniques. During this experiment, you will perform these tests on six known anions.

Then, two "unknown" solutions, each containing one of the six anions, will be analyzed. When an unknown is analyzed, the results should agree in all respects with one of the known anions. If the results do not fully agree with one of the six known ions, either the testing has been poorly done or the unknown does not contain any of the specified ions.

Three different kinds of equations may be used to express the behavior of ions in solution. For example, the reaction of the chloride ion (from sodium chloride) may be written.

1. $NaCl(aq) + AgNO_3(aq) \longrightarrow AgCl(s) + NaNO_3(aq)$

2. $Na^+(aq) + Cl^-(aq) + Ag^+(aq) + NO_3^-(aq) \longrightarrow AgCl(s) + Na^+(aq) + NO_3^-(aq)$

3. $Cl^-(aq) + Ag^+(aq) \longrightarrow AgCl(s)$

Equation (1) is the **formula (un-ionized) equation;** it shows the formulas of the substances in the equation as they are normally written. Equation (2) is the **total ionic equation;** it shows the substances as they occur in solution. Strong electrolytes are written as ions; weak electrolytes, precipitates, and gases are written in their un-ionized or molecular form. Equation (3) is the **net ionic equation;** it includes only those substances or ions in Equation (2) that have undergone a chemical change. Thus Na^+ and NO_3^- (sometimes called the "spectator" ions) have not changed and do not appear in the net ionic equation. In both the total ionic and net ionic equations, the atoms and charges must be balanced.

PROCEDURE

Wear protective glasses

1. Clean eight test tubes and rinse each twice with 5 mL of distilled water. The first six test tubes are for the known solutions that will be tested to demonstrate the expected reactions with each anion. Use a marker to label these tubes as follows: NaCl, NaBr, NaI, Na_2SO_4, Na_3PO_4 and Na_2CO_3. The last two tubes are for your unknowns and should be left blank for now. Arrange these test tubes in order in your test tube rack.

2. Clean and rinse two more test tubes and take them to your instructor for your unknown solutions and their identification code. Label them with the code numbers immediately. To avoid possible confusion with the empty unknown test tubes in the rack, put these coded tubes aside in a beaker. Record the code of these unknowns in the top right-hand columns of your report form and label each of the blank tubes in the rack with one of these unknown code numbers.

Pour 2 mL (no more) of each of the six known solutions—one solution per tube—and 2 mL of the corresponding unknown into each unknown tube. Save the remaining portions of the unknown solutions for tests B and C.

You can save considerable time by measuring out 2 mL into the first test tube and using the height of this liquid in the test tube as a guide for measuring out the others.

 Dispose of solutions containing decane in the container marked "Waste organic solvents." Dispose of solutions containing silver, and barium, in the "heavy metals waste" container.

For each of the following tests that will be performed on known and unknown solutions, there is a corresponding block on the report form where observations should be recorded. If a precipitate forms, record "ppt formed" and include its color. If no precipitate forms, record "no ppt." When dissolving precipitates, record "ppt dissolved" or "ppt did not dissolve." For the decane solubility test, indicate the color of the decane layer.

A. Silver Nitrate Test

 Silver nitrate will stain your skin black. If any silver nitrate gets on your hands, wash it off immediately to avoid these stains.

Add about 1 mL of 0.1 M silver nitrate solution to each test tube. Record the results. Now add about 3 mL of dilute (6 M) nitric acid to each test tube; stopper and shake well. Record the results.

B. Barium Chloride Test

Wash all eight test tubes and rinse each tube twice with distilled water. Again put about 2 mL of the specified solution into each of the eight test tubes. Add about 2 mL of 0.1 M barium chloride solution to each test tube and mix. Record the results. Now add 3 mL of dilute hydrochloric acid to each tube; stopper and shake well. Record the results.

C. Organic Solvent Test

Again wash and rinse all eight test tubes. Again put about 2 mL of the specified solution into each of the eight test tubes. Now add about 2 mL of decane and about 2 mL of chlorine water to each test tube; stopper and shake well. Record the results.

After completing the three tests, compare the results of the known solutions with your observations for your unknown solutions. Record the formula of the anion present in each solution on the report form (Part D).

REPORT FOR EXPERIMENT 14

Identification of Selected Anions

	NaCl	NaBr	NaI	Na_2SO_4	Na_3PO_4	Na_2CO_3	Unknown No. ___	Unknown No. ___
A. AgNO₃ Test Addition of AgNO₃ solution								
Addition of dil. HNO₃								
B. BaCl₂ Test Addition of BaCl₂ solution								
Addition of dil. HCl								
C. Organic Solvent Test Color of decane layer								
D. Formula of anion present in the solution tested.								

QUESTIONS AND PROBLEMS

1. The following three solutions were analyzed according to the scheme used in this experiment. Which one, if any, of the ions tested, is present in each solution? If the data indicate that none of the six is present, write the word "None" as your answer.

(a) **Silver Nitrate Test.** Yellow precipitate formed, which dissolved in dilute nitric acid.

Barium Chloride Test. White precipitate formed, which dissolved in dilute hydrochloric acid.

Organic Solvent Test. The decane layer remained almost colorless after treatment with chlorine water.

Anion present _____

(b) **Silver Nitrate Test.** Red precipitate formed, which dissolved in dilute nitric acid to give an orange solution.

Barium Chloride Test. Yellow precipitate formed, which dissolved in dilute hydrochloric acid to give an orange solution.

Organic Solvent Test. The decane layer remained almost colorless after treatment with chlorine water.

Anion present _____

(c) **Silver Nitrate Test.** Yellow precipitate formed, which did not dissolve in dilute nitric acid.

Barium Chloride Test. No precipitate formed.

Organic Solvent Test. The decane layer turned reddish-brown.

Anion present _____

2. Write formula, total ionic, and net ionic equations for the following reactions: Use the solubility table in Appendix 5 for reactions that were not observed directly in this experiment. All reactions are in aqueous solutions.

   (a) Sodium bromide and silver nitrate.

   (b) Sodium carbonate and silver nitrate.

   (c) Sodium arsenate and barium chloride.

3. Write net ionic equations for the following reactions. Assume that a precipitate is formed in each case.

   (a) Sodium iodide and silver nitrate.

   (b) Sodium acetate and silver nitrate.

   (c) Sodium phosphate and barium chloride.

   (d) Sodium sulfate and barium chloride.

EXPERIMENT 15

Quantitative Preparation of Potassium Chloride

MATERIALS AND EQUIPMENT

Solid: potassium bicarbonate ($KHCO_3$). **Solution:** 6 M hydrochloric acid (HCl).

DISCUSSION

In this experiment you will examine and verify the mole and mass relationships involved in the quantitative preparation of potassium chloride. Potassium bicarbonate is the source of the potassium ion, and hydrochloric acid is the source of chloride ions. The reaction is expressed in the following equation, which shows that potassium bicarbonate and hydrochloric acid react with each other in a 1-to-1-mole ratio:

$$KHCO_3(aq) + HCl(aq) \longrightarrow KCl(aq) + H_2O(l) + CO_2(g)$$

Furthermore, for every mole of potassium bicarbonate present, 1 mole of potassium chloride is formed. From these molar relationships we can calculate the amount of potassium chloride that is theoretically obtainable from any specified amount of potassium bicarbonate in the reaction. The experimental value can then be compared to the theoretical value.

To conduct the experiment quantitatively, we need to react all the potassium ion from a known amount of potassium bicarbonate and to isolate the KCl in pure a form as feasible. To ensure complete reaction of the potassium bicarbonate, an excess of hydrochloric acid is used The end of the reaction is detectable because the evolution of the gaseous product CO_2 stops when all the $KHCO_3$ has been reacted.

Use the following relationships in your calculations:

1. 1 mole $KHCO_3$ reacted = 1 mole HCl reacted = 1 mole KCl produced

2. 1 mole of solute = 1 molar mass of solute

    Example: $\text{moles } KHCO_3 = (\text{g } KHCO_3)\left(\dfrac{1 \text{ mol } KHCO_3}{100.1 \text{ g } KHCO_3}\right)$

3. Molarity $= \dfrac{\text{moles solute}}{\text{L solution}}$ and for the HCl used in this reaction we can set up the conversion factors

$$\frac{6.0 \text{ mol HCl}}{1 \text{ L}} \quad \text{or} \quad \frac{6.0 \text{ mol HCl}}{1000 \text{ mL}}$$

Note that molarity is an expression of concentration, the units of which are *always* moles of solute per liter of solution from which conversions factors for mol $\longleftrightarrow$ volume can be derived.

For example, if you wanted to determine the volume of 2.0 M HCl that would be used to complete the reaction with 5.5000 g of $KHCO_3$, the dimensional analysis setup would be:

$$mL\, HCl = (5.5000\, g\, KHCO_3)\left(\frac{1\, mole\, KHCO_3}{100.1\, g\, KHCO_3}\right)\left(\frac{1\, mol\, HCl}{1\, mol\, KHCO_3}\right)\left(\frac{1000\, mL}{2.0\, mol\, HCl}\right) = 27\, mL\, HCl$$

4. Percentage error $= \left(\dfrac{\text{theoretical value} - \text{experimental value}}{\text{theoretical value}}\right)(100)$

The sequence of major experimental steps in this experiment is as follows:

1. Weigh an evaporating dish.

2. Weigh 2-3 g potassium bicarbonate into the evaporating dish.

3. Dissolve potassium bicarbonate in 5 mL distilled water.

4. Add hydrocholoric acid solution slowly until the fizzing stops.

5. Evaporate the liquid to obtain the dry product, KCl.

6. Heat and dry the KCl to constant weight.

7. Determine the mass of KCl produced.

PROCEDURE

Wear protective glasses.

> 1. Make all weighings *to the highest precision* possible with the balance available.
>
> 2. Use the same balance for all weighings.
>
> 3. Record all data directly on the report form as they are obtained.

1. Weigh a clean, dry evaporating dish.

2. Now add between 2 and 3 g (no more) of potassium bicarbonate to the evaporating dish and reweigh.

3. Dissolve the potassium bicarbonate in 5 mL of distilled water. If all the potassium bicarbonate does not completely dissolve, do not worry about it. Continue on with the next step.

4. In a graduated cylinder, obtain 6.0 mL of 6 M HCl and **slowly, *with* stirring,** add it to the bicarbonate solution. (The product is formed in this step).

5. Using a beaker of water to make a water bath as shown in Experiment 1, Part C, evaporate the liquid from the solution of potassium chloride. Replenish the water in the water bath as needed. When the water has essentially evaporated (the residue in the dish

looks dry), allow the system to cool for a few minutes; remove the evaporating dish and thoroughly dry the bottom of the dish.

6. The following method of drying the product must be followed to avoid spattering and loss of product. Pay attention during this procedure. Do not leave the drying setup unattended.

   Adjust the burner so you have a nonluminous, 10 to 15 cm (4 to 6 in.) flame **without a distinct inner cone.** Place the evaporating dish on a wire gauze 4-6 in. above the top of the barrel. Heat the dish and contents for 5-10 minutes (the KCl should appear dry). Touch the surface with a stirring rod to prevent the formation of a crust. If spattering occurs remove the burner momentarily and either lower the flame or raise the dish before continuing heating.

7. Cool the dish, weigh, and reheat for an additional 5 minutes. Cool again and reweigh. If the second weighing is within 0.08 g of the first, the KCl may be considered dry. If the second weighing has decreased more than 0.08 g, a third heating (5 minutes) and weighing is necessary. The experiment is complete after obtaining constant weight (within 0.08 g). If constant weight is not obtained after three heatings, your instructor will provide instructions on what to do.

8. From the data collected, determine the mass of KCl produced.

 9. Dissolve the KCl in water and wash it down the sink.

REPORT FOR EXPERIMENT 15

Quantitative Preparation of Potassium Chloride

A. Write the balanced equation for the reaction between $KHCO_3$ and HCl:

B. Experimental Data and Calculations: Record all measurement to the highest precision of the balance and remember to use the proper number of significant figures in all calculations. (The number 0.004 has only *one* significant figure.)

1. Mass of empty evaporating dish   _____ g

2. Mass of dish and dry $KHCO_3$ _____ g

3. Mass of dish and residue (KCl) after first heating   _____ g

4. Mass of dish and residue (KCl) after second heating   _____ g

5. Mass of dish and residue (KCl) after third heating (if necessary)   _____ g

6. Mass of potassium bicarbonate   _____ g
   show calculation set-up

7. Moles of potassium bicarbonate   _____ mol
   show calculation set-up

8. Experimental mass of potassium chloride obtained   _____ g
   show calculation set-up

9. Experimental moles of potassium chloride obtained   _____ mol
   show calculation set-up

10. Theoretical moles of KCl   _____ mol
    show calculation set-up

11. Theoretical mass of KCl   _____ g
    show calculation set-up

12. Percentage error for experimental mass of KCl vs.   _____ %
    theoretical mass of KCl (show calculation set-up)

QUESTIONS AND PROBLEMS

1. What was done in the experiment to make sure that all the $KHCO_3$ was reacted?

2. Why is the mass of KCl recovered less than the starting mass of $KHCO_3$?

3. Calculate the moles and grams of HCl present in the 6.0 mL of 6.0 M HCl solution you used.

_____ mol HCl

_____ g HCl

4. Would the 6.0 mL of 6.0 M HCl be sufficient to react with 3.80 g $KHCO_3$? Show supporting calculations and explanation.

5. Theoretically, why should the moles of $KHCO_3$ and the moles of KCl produced be the same?

6. If 3.000 g of K_2CO_3 were used in this experiment (instead of $KHCO_3$),

   (a) What is the balanced equation for the reaction?

   (b) How many milliliters of 6.0 M HCl would be needed   _____ mL HCl

   (c) How many grams of KCl would be formed in the reaction?   _____ g KCl

EXPERIMENT 17

Lewis Structures and Molecular Models

MATERIALS AND EQUIPMENT

Special equipment: Ball-and-stick molecular model sets

DISCUSSION

Molecules are stable groups of covalently bonded atoms, usually nonmetallic atoms. Chemists study models of molecules to learn more about their bonds, the spatial relationships between atoms and the shapes of molecules. Using models helps us to predict molecular structure.

A. Valence Electrons

Every atom has a nucleus surrounded by electrons which are held within a region of space by the attractive force of the positive protons in the nucleus. The electrons in the outermost energy level of an atom are called valence electrons. The **valence electrons** are involved in bonding atoms together to form compounds. For the representative elements, the number of valence electrons in the outermost energy level is the same as their group number in the periodic table (Groups 1A–7A). For example, sulfur in Group 6A has six valence electrons and potassium in Group 1A has one valence electron.

B. Lewis Structures

Lewis electron dot structures are a useful device for keeping track of valence electrons for the representative elements. In this notation, the nucleus and core electrons are represented by the atomic symbol and the valence electrons are represented by dots around the symbol. Although there are exceptions, Lewis structures emphasize an octet of electrons arranged in the noble gas configuration, ns^2np^6. Lewis structures can be drawn for individual atoms, monatomic ions, molecules, and polyatomic ions.

1. **Atoms and Monatomic Ions:**   A Lewis structure for an atom shows its symbol surrounded by dots to represent its valence electrons. Monatomic ions form when an atom loses or gains electrons to achieve a noble gas electron configuration. The Lewis structure for a monatomic ion is enclosed by brackets with the charge of the ion shown. The symbol is surrounded by the valence electrons with the number adjusted for the electrons lost or gained when the ion is formed. This is the basis of ionic bond formation which is not included in this experiment.

Examples:

sulfur atom	sulfide ion	potassium atom	potassium ion
$\cdot\ddot{\underset{\cdot\cdot}{\text{S}}}\cdot$	$[:\ddot{\underset{\cdot\cdot}{\text{S}}}:]^{2-}$	K·	$[\text{K}]^+$

2. **Molecules and Polyatomic Ions:**   Lewis structures for molecules and polyatomic ions emphasize the principle that atoms in covalently bonded groups achieve the noble gas configuration, ns^2np^6. Since all noble gases except helium have eight valence electrons, this is

often called the octet rule. Although many molecules and ions have structures which support the octet rule, it is only a guideline. There are many exceptions. One major exception is the hydrogen atom which can covalently bond with only one atom and share a total of two electrons to form a noble gas configuration like helium. All of the examples in this experiment follow the octet rule except hydrogen.

A Lewis structure for covalently bonded atoms is a two-dimensional model in which one pair of shared electrons between two atoms is a single covalent bond represented by a short line; unshared or lone pairs of electrons are shown as dots. Sometimes two pairs of electrons are shared between two atoms forming a double bond and are represented by two short lines. It is even possible for two atoms to share three pairs of electrons forming a triple bond, represented by three short lines. For a polyatomic ion, the rules are the same except that the group of atoms is enclosed in brackets and the overall charge of the ion is shown. For example:

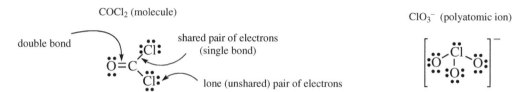

The rules for writing Lewis structures for molecules and polyatomic ions will be provided in the procedure section so you can use your Lewis structures to build three-dimensional models.

C. Molecular Model Building

The three-dimensional structure of a molecule is difficult to visualize from a two-dimensional Lewis structure. Therefore, in this experiment, a ball-and-stick model kit (molecular "tinker toys") is used to build models so the common geometric patterns into which atoms are arranged can be seen. Each model that is constructed must be checked by the instructor and described by its geometry and its bond angles on the report form.

D. Molecular Geometry

Atoms in a molecule or polyatomic ion are arranged into geometric patterns that allow their electron pairs to get as far away from each other as possible (which minimizes the repulsive forces between them). The theory underlying this molecular model is known as the valence shell electron pair repulsion (**VSEPR**) **theory.** All of the geometric structures in this experiment fall into the following patterns:

1. **Tetrahedral:** four pairs of shared electrons (no pairs of lone (unshared) electrons) around a central atom.

2. **Trigonal pyramidal:** three pairs of shared electrons and one pair of unshared electrons around a central atom.

3. **Trigonal planar:** three groups of shared electrons around a central atom. Two of these groups are single bonds and one group is a double bond made up of two pairs of shared electrons. There are no unshared electrons around the central atom.

4. **Bent:** two groups of shared electrons (in single or double bonds) and one or two pairs of unshared electrons around a central atom.

5. **Linear:** two groups of shared electrons, usually double bonds with two shared electron pairs between two atoms, and no unshared electrons around a central atom. When there are only two atoms in a molecule or ion, and there is no central atom (HBr, for example), the geometry is also linear. These patterns are described more extensively in Section E, which follows.

> **NOTE:** There are other electron arrangements and molecular geometries. Since they do not follow the octet rule, they are not included in this experiment.

E. Bond Angles

Bond angles always refer to the angle formed between two end atoms with respect to the central atom. If there is no central atom, there is no bond angle.

Central atom ⟶ Bond angle

The size of the angle depends mainly on the repulsive forces of the electrons around the central atom. The molecular model kits are designed so that these angles can be determined when sticks representing electron pairs are inserted into pre-drilled holes.

1. Bond angles for atoms bonded to a central atom without unshared electrons on the central atom.

   a. For four pairs of shared electrons around a central atom (tetrahedral geometry) the angle between the bonds is approximately **109.5°**.

   b. For three atoms bonded to a central atom, (trigonal planar) the angle is **120°**. The shared electron pairs can be arranged in single or double bonds.

   c. For two atoms bonded to a central atom (linear) the angle is **180°**. The shared electrons are usually arranged in double bonds.

   d. Linear diatomic molecules or ions with no central atom do not have a bond angle.

2. Bond angles for atoms bonded to a central atom **with** unshared electrons on the central atom.

When some of the valence electrons around a central atom are unshared, the VSEPR theory can be used to predict changes in spatial arrangements. An unshared pair of electrons on the central atom has a strong influence on the shape of the molecule. It reduces the angle of bonding pairs by squeezing them toward each other.

For example:

tetrahedral	trigonal pyramidal	bent	bent
No unshared electrons	1 unshared electron pair	2 unshared lone pairs	1 unshared pair
4 pairs shared electrons	3 pairs shared electrons	2 pairs shared electrons	2 groups shared electrons
CH_4	NH_3	H_2O	

repulsive force on shared e⁻ increases, which pushes down on H atoms	repulsive force on shared e⁻ increases, which pushes down on peripheral atoms

F. Bond Polarity

Electrons shared by two atoms are influenced by the positive attractive forces of both atomic nuclei. For like atoms, these forces are equal. For example, in diatomic molecules such as H_2 or Cl_2 the bonded atoms have exactly the same electronegativity (affinity for the bonding electrons). Electronegativity values for most of the elements have been assigned.

Electronegativity Table

* The electronegativity value is given below the symbol of each element.

In general, electronegativity increases as we move across a period and up a group on the periodic table. Identical atoms with identical attractions for their shared electron pairs form **nonpolar covalent bonds.** Unlike atoms exert unequal attractions for their shared electrons and form **polar covalent bonds.**

Electronegativity is used to determine the direction of bond polarity which can be indicated in the Lewis structure by replacing the short line for the bond with a modified arrow (⟵⟶) pointed towards the more electronegative atom. For example, nitrogen and hydrogen have electronegativity values of 3.0 and 2.1, respectively. The N—H bond is thus represented as

N $\longleftrightarrow$ H with the arrow directed toward the more electronegative nitrogen atom. Then, the Lewis structure can be redrawn with arrows replacing the dashes as shown for NH_4^+ and NH_3.

$$\left[\begin{array}{c} H \\ \updownarrow \\ H \leftrightarrow N \leftarrow H \\ \updownarrow \\ H \end{array} \right]^+ \qquad\qquad H \nearrow \overset{\cdot\cdot}{\underset{\uparrow}{N}} \nwarrow H$$

G. Molecular Dipoles

When there are several polar covalent bonds within a molecule or a polyatomic ion such as in NH_3 and NH_4^+ the polar effect of these bonds around a central atom can be cancelled if they are arranged **symmetrically** as shown in CCl_4 below. On the other hand, if the arrangement of the polar bonds is asymmetrical, as in the bent water molecule, H_2O, the resulting molecule has a definite positive end and oppositely charged negative end, and the molecule is called a dipole. In water, the H atoms have a partial positive charge, δ^+, and the O atom has a partial negative charge, δ^-. The symmetry, or lack of symmetry of molecules and polyatomic ions, can generally be seen in the three-dimensional model.

$$\begin{array}{c} :\overset{\cdot\cdot}{Cl}: \\ \uparrow \\ :\overset{\cdot\cdot}{Cl} \leftarrow C \rightarrow \overset{\cdot\cdot}{Cl}: \\ \downarrow \\ :\overset{\cdot\cdot}{Cl}: \end{array} \qquad\qquad \begin{array}{c} \delta^- \\ \overset{\cdot\cdot}{\underset{}{O}} \\ H \nearrow \quad \nwarrow H \\ \delta^+ \qquad \delta^+ \end{array}$$

PROCEDURE

Follow steps **A–G** for each of the molecules or polyatomic ions listed on the report form. Refer back to the previous discussion, organized into corresponding sections A–G, for help with each step if necessary.

A. Number of Valence Electrons in a Molecule or Polyatomic Ion

Use a periodic table to determine the number of valence electrons for each group of atoms in the first column of the report form.

example: SiF_4 Si is in Group 4A, it has 4 valence electrons
                     F is in Group 7A, it has 7 valence electrons

     Total valence electrons is $4 + 4(7) = 32$ electrons

If the group is a polyatomic ion, total the electrons as above, then add one electron for each negative charge or subtract one electron for each positive charge.

example: CO_3^{2-} C is in group 4A, it has 4 valence electrons
                     O is in Group 6A, it has 6 valence electrons
                     Ion has a -2 charge, add 2 electrons

     Total valence electrons is $4 + 3(6) + 2 = 24$ electrons

B. Lewis Structures for Molecules and Polyatomic Ions

Use the following rules to show the two-dimensional Lewis structure for each molecule or polyatomic ion. Put your structure in the space provided. Use a *sharp* pencil and be as neat as possible.

1. Write down the skeletal arrangement of the atoms and connect them with a single covalent bond (a short line). We want to keep the rules at a minimum for this step, but we also want to avoid arrangements which will later prove incorrect. Useful guidelines are

     a. carbon is usually a central atom or forms bonds with itself; if carbon is absent, the central atom is usually the least electronegative atom in the group;

     b. hydrogen, which has only one valence electron, can form only one covalent bond and is never a central atom;

     c. oxygen atoms are not normally bonded to each other except in peroxides, and oxygen atoms normally have a maximum of two covalent bonds (two single bonds or one double bond).

Using these guidelines, skeletal arrangements for SiF_4 and CO_3^{2-} are

$$
\begin{array}{cc}
\begin{array}{c}
\text{F} \\
| \\
\text{F}-\text{Si}-\text{F} \\
| \\
\text{F}
\end{array}
&
\begin{array}{c}
\text{O}-\text{C}-\text{O} \\
| \\
\text{O}
\end{array}
\end{array}
$$

2. Subtract two electrons from the total valence electrons for each single bond used in the skeletal arrangement. This calculation gives the net number of electrons available for completing the electron structure. In the examples above, there are 4 and 3 single bonds, respectively. With 2 e$^-$ per bond the calculation is

SiF_4: 32 e$^-$ − 4(2 e$^-$) = 24 e$^-$ left to be assigned to the molecule

CO_3^{2-}: 24 e$^-$ − 3(2 e$^-$) = 18 e$^-$ left to be assigned to the polyatomic ion

3. Distribute these remaining electrons as pairs of dots around each atom (except hydrogen) to give each atom a total of eight electrons around it. If there are not enough electrons available, move on to step 4.

$$
\begin{array}{cc}
\begin{array}{c}
\text{:F:} \\
| \\
\text{:F}-\text{Si}-\text{F:} \\
| \\
\text{:F:}
\end{array}
&
\begin{array}{c}
\text{:O}-\text{C}-\text{O:} \\
| \\
\text{:O:}
\end{array}
\end{array}
$$

all atoms have 8 electrons so the Lewis structure is complete

C does not have an octet of electrons so it is necessary to continue on with step 4

4. Check each Lewis structure to determine if every atom except hydrogen has an octet of electrons. If there are not enough electrons to give each of these atoms eight electrons, change single bonds between atoms to double or triple bonds by shifting unshared pairs of electrons as needed. A double bond counts as 4 e$^-$ for each atom to which it is bonded.

For CO_3^{2-}, shift $2\,e^-$ from one of the O atoms and place it between C and that O.

$$\left[\overset{..}{\underset{..}{O}}-C\overset{\frown}{\underset{\underset{..}{\overset{|}{\underset{..}{O}}}}{\overset{..}{O}}}\right]^{2-} \longrightarrow \left[\overset{..}{\underset{..}{O}}-C\underset{\underset{..}{\overset{|}{\underset{..}{O}}}}{=}\overset{..}{\underset{..}{O}}\right]^{2-}$$

Now, all the atoms have $8e^-$ around them. (Don't forget the $^{2-}$)

C. Model Building

1. Use the balls and sticks from the kit provided to build a 3-dimensional model of the molecule or polyatomic ion for each Lewis structure in the report form.

   a. Use a ball with 4 holes for the central atom.

   b. Use inflexible sticks for single bonds.

   c. Use flexible connectors for double or triple bonds.

   d. Use inflexible sticks for lone pairs around the central atom only.

2. **Leave the model together until it is checked by the instructor.** If you have to wait for someone to check your model, start building the next model on the list. If you complete each structure so fast that you run out of components before someone checks your models, work on other parts of the experiment.

D. Molecular Geometry

Look at your model from all angles and compare its structure to the description in the discussion (Section D). Then identify its molecular geometry from the following list and write the name of the geometric pattern on the report form in column D.

   1. tetrahedral

   2. trigonal pyramidal

   3. trigonal planar

   4. bent

   5. linear

E. Central Bond Angles

Fill in column E with the bond angles between the central atom and all atoms attached to it. Review the discussion (Section E) to find the value of the angles associated with each geometric form. For molecules with more than one central atom, give bond angles for each. For molecules without a central atom and hence no bond angle, write *no central atom*.

F. Bond Polarity

Bond polarity can be determined by looking up the electronegativity values for both atoms in the Electronegativity table. In the F column of the report form, draw the symbols for both atoms involved in a bond and connect them with an arrow pointing toward the more electronegative atom. If there are several identical bonds it is only necessary to draw one. Use the following as examples.

$$N \leftarrow H \qquad\qquad S \leftrightarrow O$$

G. Molecular Dipoles

Look at the model and evaluate its symmetry. Decide if the polar bonds within it cancel each other around the central atom resulting in a nonpolar molecule or if they do not cancel one another and result in a dipole. Some examples:

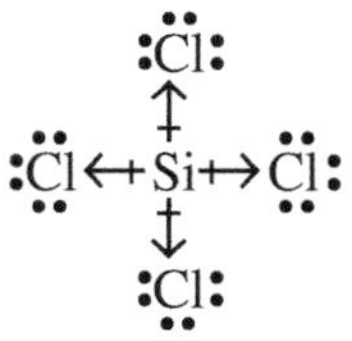

:Cl:
↑
:Cl: ← Si → :Cl:
↓
:Cl:

symmetrical
nonpolar

H
↓
H → C → :Cl:
↑
H

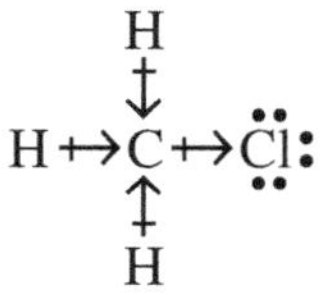

asymmetrical
a dipole

Remember, it is also possible for all the polar bonds within a polyatomic ion to cancel each other so the resultant effect is nonpolar even though the group as a whole has a net charge.

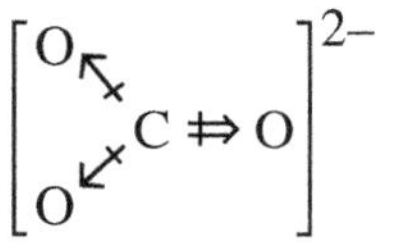

$$\left[\begin{array}{c} O \\ C \Rrightarrow O \\ O \end{array} \right]^{2-}$$

symmetrical
not a dipole

REPORT FOR EXPERIMENT 17

Lewis Structures and Molecular Models

For each of the following molecules or polyatomic ions, fill out columns A through G using the instructions provided in the procedure section. These instructions are summarized briefly below.

A. Calculate the total number of valence electrons in each formula.
B. Draw a Lewis structure for the molecule or ion which satisfies the rules provided in the procedure.
C. Build a model of the molecule and have it checked by the instructor.
D. Use your model to determine the molecular geometry for this molecule (don't try to guess the geometry without the model): tetrahedral, trigonal pyramidal, trigonal planar, bent, linear
E. Determine the bond angle between the central atom and the atoms bonded to it. If there are only two atoms in the structure write "no central atom" in the space provided.
F. Use the electronegativity table to determine the electronegativity of the bonded atoms.
   If the bonds are polar, indicate this with a modified arrow ($\longmapsto$) pointing to the more electronegative element.
   If the bonds are nonpolar, indicate this with a short line (—).
   If there are two or more different atoms bonded to the central atom, include each bond.
G. Use your model and your knowledge of the bond polarity to determine if the molecule as a whole is nonpolar or a dipole.
   If it is polar, write *dipole* in G. If it is not, write *nonpolar*.

Molecule or Polyatomic Ion	A No. of Valence Electrons	B Lewis Structure	C	D Molecular Geometry	E Bond Angles	F Bond Polarity	G Molecular Dipole or Nonpolar
CH_4							
CS_2							

	A	B	C	D	E	F	G
Molecule or Polyatomic Ion	No. of Valence Electrons	Lewis Structure		Molecular Geometry	Bond Angles	Bond Polarity	Molecular Dipole or Nonpolar
H_2S							
N_2							
SO_4^{2-}							
H_3O^+							
CH_3Cl							
C_2H_6							
C_2H_4							

No. of Molecule or Polyatomic Ion	A Valence Electrons	B Lewis Structure	C	D Molecular Geometry	E Bond Angles	F Bond Polarity	G Molecular Dipole or Nonpolar
$C_2H_2Cl_2$		*					
SO_3^{2-}							
CH_2O							
OF_2							
NO_2^-							
O_2							
NO_3^-		**					

*More than one possible Lewis structure can be drawn. See questions 1, 2.
**More than one possible Lewis structure can be drawn. See question 3.

QUESTIONS

1. There are three acceptable Lewis structures for $C_2H_2Cl_2$ (*) and you have drawn one of them on the report form. Draw the other two structures and indicate whether each one is nonpolar or a dipole.

2. Explain why one of the three structures for $C_2H_2Cl_2$ is nonpolar and the other two are molecular dipoles.

3. There are three Lewis structures for $[NO_3]^-$ (**). Draw the two structures which are not on the report form. Compare the molecular polarity of the three structures.

EXPERIMENT 19

Charles' Law

MATERIALS AND EQUIPMENT

125 mL Erlenmeyer flask, one-hole rubber stopper, glass and rubber tubing, pneumatic trough, thermometer, screw clamp.

DISCUSSION

The quantitative relationship between the volume and the absolute temperature of a gas is summarized in Charles' law. This law states: at constant pressure, the volume of a particular sample of gas is directly proportional to the absolute temperature.

Charles' law may be expressed mathematically:

$$V \propto T \qquad \text{(constant pressure)} \qquad (1)$$

$$V = kT \quad \text{or} \quad \frac{V}{T} = k \quad \text{(constant pressure)} \qquad (2)$$

where V is volume, T is Kelvin temperature, and k is a proportionality constant dependent on the number of moles and the pressure of the gas.

If the volume of the same sample of gas is measured at two temperatures, $V_1/T_1 = k$ and $V_2/T_2 = k$, and we may say that

$$\frac{V_1}{T_1} = \frac{V_2}{T_2} \quad \text{or} \quad V_2 = (V_1)\left(\frac{T_2}{T_1}\right) \qquad \text{(constant pressure)} \qquad (3)$$

where V_1 and T_1 represent one set of conditions and V_2 and T_2 a different set of conditions, with pressure the same at both conditions.

Experimental Verification of Charles' Law

This experiment measures the volume of an air sample at two temperatures, a high temperature, T_H, and a low temperature, T_L. The volume of the air sample at the high temperature, (V_H), decreases when the sample is cooled to the low temperature and becomes V_L. All of these measurements are made directly. The experimental data is then used to verify Charles' law by two methods:

1. The experimental volume (V_{exp}) measured at the low temperature is compared to the V_L predicted by Charles' law where

$$V_L(theoretical) = (V_H)\left(\frac{T_L}{T_H}\right)$$

2. The V/T ratios for the air sample measured at both the high and the low temperatures are compared. Charles' law predicts that these ratios will be equal.

$$\frac{V_H}{T_H} = \frac{V_L}{T_L}$$

Pressure Considerations

The relationship between temperature and volume defined by Charles' law is valid only if the pressure is the same when the volume is measured at each temperature. That is not the case in this experiment.

1. The volume, V_H, of air at the higher temperature, T_H, is measured at atmospheric pressure, P_{atm} in a dry Erlenmeyer flask. The air is assumed to be dry and the pressure is obtained from a barometer.

2. The experimental air volume, (V_{exp}) at the lower temperature, T_L, is measured over water. This volume is saturated with water vapor that contributes to the total pressure in the flask. Therefore, the experimental volume must be corrected to the volume of dry air at atmospheric pressure. This is done using Boyle's law as follows:

   a. The partial pressure of the dry air, P_{DA}, is calculated by subtracting the vapor pressure of water from atmospheric pressure:

   $$P_{DA} = P_{atm} - P_{H_2O}$$

   b. The volume that this dry air would occupy at P_{atm} is then calculated using the Boyle's law equation:

   $$(V_{DA})(P_{atm}) = (V_{exp})(P_{DA})$$
   $$(V_{DA}) = \frac{(V_{exp})(P_{DA})}{(P_{atm})}$$

PROCEDURE

Wear protective glasses.

 No waste for disposal in this experiment.

> **NOTE:** It is essential that the Erlenmeyer flask and rubber stopper assembly be as dry as possible in order to obtain reproducible results.

Dry a 125 mL Erlenmeyer flask by gently heating the entire outer surface with a burner flame. Care must be used in heating to avoid breaking the flask. If the flask is wet, first wipe the inner and outer surfaces with a towel to remove nearly all the water. Then, holding the flask with a test tube holder, gently heat the entire flask. Avoid placing the flask directly in the flame. Allow to cool.

While the flask is cooling select a 1-hole rubber stopper to fit the flask and insert a 5 cm piece of glass tubing into the stopper so that the end of the tubing is flush with the bottom of the stopper. Attach a 3 cm piece of rubber tubing to the glass tubing (see Figure 19.1). Insert the stopper into the flask and mark (wax pencil) the distance that it is inserted. Clamp the flask so that it is submerged as far as possible in water contained in a 400 mL beaker (without the flask touching the bottom of the beaker) (see Figure 19.2).

Heat the water to boiling. Keep the flask in the gently boiling water for at least 8 minutes to allow the air in the flask to attain the temperature of the boiling water. Add water as needed to maintain the water level in the beaker. Read and record the temperature of the boiling water.

While the flask is still in the boiling water, seal it by clamping the rubber tubing tightly with a screw clamp. Remove the flask from the hot water and submerge it in a pan of cold water, keeping the top down at all times to avoid losing air (see Figure 19.3). Remove the screw clamp, letting the cold water flow into the flask. Keep the flask totally submerged for about 6 minutes to allow the flask and contents to attain the temperature of the water. Read and record the temperature of the water in the pan.

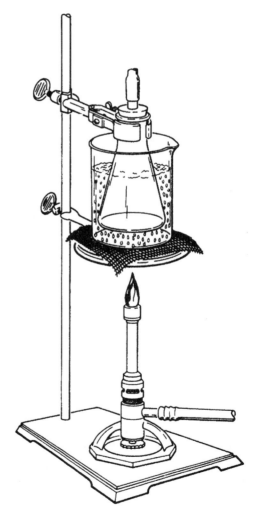

Figure 19.2   Heating the flask (and air) in boiling water

Figure 19.1   Rubber stopper assembly

In order to equalize the pressure inside the flask with that of the atmosphere, bring the water level in the flask to the same level as the water in the pan by raising or lowering the flask (see Figure 19.3). With the water levels equal, pinch the rubber tubing to close the flask. Remove the flask from the water and set it down on the laboratory bench.

Using a graduated cylinder carefully measure and record the volume of water in the flask.

Repeat the entire experiment. Use the same flask and flame dry again; **make sure that the rubber stopper assembly is thoroughly dried inside and outside.**

After the second trial fill the flask to the brim with water and insert the stopper assembly to the mark, letting the glass and rubber fill to the top and overflow. Measure the volume of water in the flask. Since this volume is the total volume of the flask, record it as the volume of air at the higher temperature. Because the same flask is used in both trials, it is necessary to make this measurement only once.

Figure 19.3 **Equalizing the pressure in the flask. The water level inside the flask is adjusted to the level of the water in the pan by raising or lowering the flask**

REPORT FOR EXPERIMENT 19

Charles' Law

Data Table

	Trial 1	Trial 2
Temperature of boiling water, T_H	_____°C, _____K	_____°C, _____K
Temperature of cold water, T_L	_____°C, _____K	_____°C, _____K
Volume of water collected in flask (decrease in the volume of air due to cooling)		
Volume of air at higher temperature, V_H (volume of flask measured only after Trial 2)		
Volume of wet air at lower temperature (volume of flask less volume of water collected), V_{exp}		
Atmosphere pressure, P_{atm} (barometer reading)		
Vapor pressure of water at lower temperature, P_{H_2O} (see Appendix 6)		

CALCULATIONS: In the spaces below, show calculation setups for Trial 1 only. Show answers for both trials in the boxes

	Trial 1	Trial 2
1. (a)		
1. (b)		
2.		
3.		
4. (a)		
4. (b)		

1. Corrected experimental volume of dry air at the lower temperature calculated from data obtained at the lower temperature.

   (a) Pressure of dry air (P_{DA})

   $$P_{DA} = P_{Atm} - P_{H_2O}$$

   (b) Corrected experimental volume of dry air (lower temperature).

   $$V_{DA} = (V_{exp})\left(\frac{P_{DA}}{P_{Atm}}\right) =$$

2. Predicted volume of dry air at lower temperature V_L calculated by Charles' law from volume at higher temperature (V_H).

   $$V_L = (V_H)\left(\frac{T_L}{T_H}\right)$$

3. Percentage error in verification of Charles' law.

   $$\% \, error = \left(\frac{V_L - V_{DA}}{V_L}\right)(100) =$$

4. Comparison of experimental V/T ratios. (Use dry volumes and absolute temperatures.)

   (a) $\dfrac{V_H}{T_H} =$

   (b) $\dfrac{V_{DA}}{T_L} =$

– 174 –

5. On the graph paper provided, plot the volume-temperature values used in Calculation 4. Temperature data **must be in °C.** Draw a straight line between the two plotted points and extrapolate (extend) the line so that it crosses the temperature axis.

QUESTIONS AND PROBLEMS

1. (a) In the experiment, why are the water levels inside and outside the flask equalized before removing the flask from the cold water?

   (b) When the water level is higher inside than outside the flask, is the gas pressure in the flask higher than, lower than, or the same as, the atmospheric pressure? (specify which)

   _____

2. A 125 mL sample of dry air at 230°C is cooled to 100°C at constant pressure. What volume will the dry air occupy at 100°C?

   _____ mL

3. A 250 mL container of a gas is at 150°C. At what temperature will the gas occupy a volume of 125 mL, the pressure remaining constant?

   _____ °C

4. (a) An open flask of air is cooled. Answer the following:

   1. Under which conditions, before or after cooling, does the flask contain more gas molecules?

   _____

   2. Is the pressure in the flask at the lower temperature the same as, greater than, or less than the pressure in the flask before it was cooled?

   _____

(b) An open flask of air is heated, stoppered in the heated condition, and then allowed to cool back to room temperature. Answer the following:

    1. Does the flask contain the same, more, or fewer gas molecules now compared to before it was heated?

                                                     _____

    2. Is the volume occupied by the gas in the flask approximately the same, greater, or less than before it was heated?

                                                     _____

    3. Is the pressure in the flask the same, greater, or less than before the flask was heated?

                                                     _____

    4. Do any of the above conditions explain why water rushed into the flask at the lower temperature in the experiment? Amplify your answer.

5. On the graph you plotted,

    (a) At what temperature does the extrapolated line intersect the x-axis?

                                                _____ °C

    (b) At what temperature does Charles' law predict that the extrapolated line should intersect the x-axis?

                                                _____ °C

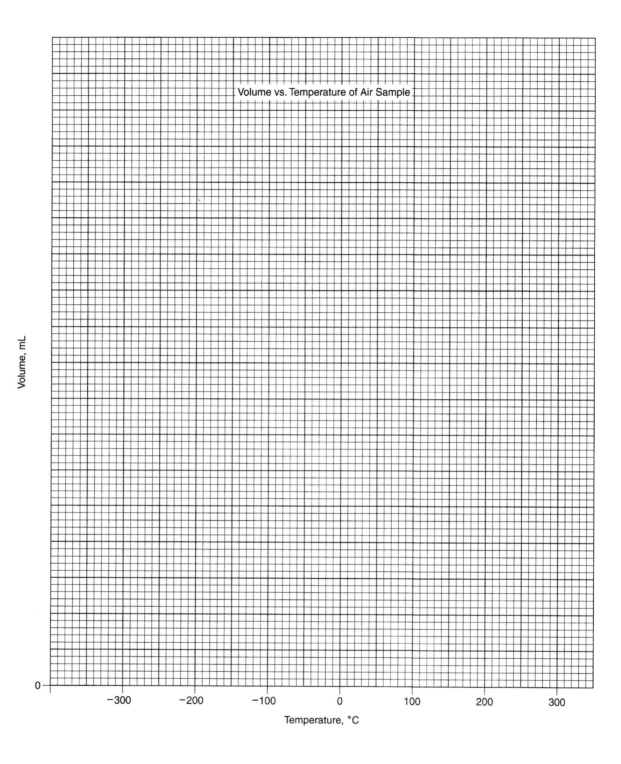

Volume vs. Temperature of Air Sample

Volume, mL

Temperature, °C

0

−300   −200   −100   0   100   200   300

EXPERIMENT 22

Neutralization–Titration I

MATERIALS AND EQUIPMENT

Solid: potassium hydrogen phthalate, abbreviated KHP ($KHC_8H_4O_4$). **Liquids:** phenolphthalein indicator, unknown base solution (NaOH). One buret (25 mL or 50 mL) and buret clamp, buret brush. Wash bottle for distilled water.

DISCUSSION

The reaction of an acid and a base to form a salt and water is known as **neutralization.** In this experiment potassium hydrogen phthalate (abbreviated KHP) is used as the acid. Potassium hydrogen phthalate is an organic substance having the formula $HKC_8H_4O_4$, and like HCl, has only one acid hydrogen atom per molecule. Because of its complex formula, potassium hydrogen phthalate is commonly called KHP Despite its complex formula we see that the reaction of KHP with sodium hydroxide is similar to that of HCl. One mole of KHP reacts with one mole of NaOH.

$$HKC_8H_4O_4 + NaOH \longrightarrow NaKC_8H_4O_4 + H_2O$$

$$HCl + NaOH \longrightarrow NaCl + H_2O$$

Titration is the process of measuring the volume of one reagent required to react with a measured volume or mass of another reagent. In this experiment we will determine the molarity of a base (NaOH) solution from data obtained by titrating KHP with the base solution. The base solution is added from a buret to a flask containing a weighed sample of KHP dissolved in water. From the mass of KHP used we calculate the moles of KHP. Exactly the same number of moles of base is needed to neutralize this number of moles of KHP since one mole of NaOH reacts with one mole of KHP. We then calculate the molarity of the base solution from the titration volume and the number of moles of NaOH in that volume.

In the titration, the point of neutralization, called the **end-point,** is observed when an indicator, placed in the solution being titrated, changes color. The indicator selected is one that changes color when the stoichiometric quantity of base (according to the chemical equation) has been added to the acid. A solution of phenolphthalein, an organic acid, is used as the indicator in this experiment. Phenolphthalein is colorless in acid solution but changes to pink when the solution becomes slightly alkaline. When the number of moles of sodium hydroxide added is equal to the number of moles of KHP originally present, the reaction is complete. The next drop of sodium hydroxide added changes the indicator from colorless to pink.

Use the following relationships in your calculations:

1. According to the equation for the reaction,

   Moles of KHP reacted = Moles of NaOH reacted

2. Moles = $\dfrac{\text{g of solute}}{\text{molar mass of solute}}$

3. Molarity is an expression of concentration, the units of which are moles of solute per liter of solution:

$$\text{Molarity} = \frac{\text{moles}}{\text{liter}}$$

Thus, a 1.00 molar (1.00 M) solution contains 1.00 mole of solute in 1 liter of solution. A 0.100 M solution, then, contains 0.100 mole of solute in 1 liter of solution.

4. The number of moles of solute present in a known volume of solution of known concentration can be calculated by multiplying the volume of the solution (in liters) by the molarity of the solution:

$$\text{Moles} = (\text{liters})(\text{molarity}) = (\text{liters})\left(\frac{\text{moles}}{\text{liter}}\right)$$

PROCEDURE

Wear protective glasses.

 Dispose of all solutions in the sink.

Make all weighings to the highest precision of the balance.

Obtain some solid KHP in a test tube or vial. Weigh two samples of KHP into 125 mL Erlenmeyer flasks, numbered for identification. (The flasks should be rinsed with distilled water, but need not be dry on the inside.) First weigh the flask, then add KHP to the flask by tapping the test tube or vial until 1.000 to 1.200 g has been added (see Figure 22.1). Determine the mass of the flask and the KHP. In a similar manner weigh another sample of KHP into the second flask. To each flask add approximately 30 mL of distilled water. If some KHP is sticking to the walls of the flask, rinse it down with water from a wash bottle. Warm the flasks slightly and swirl them until all the KHP is dissolved.

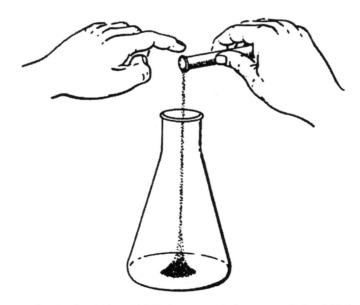

Figure 22.1   Method of adding KHP from a vial to a weighed Erlenmeyer flask

Obtain one buret and clean it. See "Use of the Buret," on the following page for instructions on cleaning and using the buret. Read and record all buret volumes to the nearest 0.01 mL.

Obtain about 250 mL of a base (NaOH) of unknown molarity in a clean, **dry** 250 mL Erlenmeyer flask as directed by your instructor. Record the number of this unknown.

1. Keep your base solution stoppered when not in use.

2. The 250 mL sample of base is intended to be used in both this experiment and Experiment 23. Be sure to label and save it.

Rinse the buret with two 5 to 10 mL portions of the base, running the second rinsing through the buret tip. Discard the rinsings in the sink. Fill the buret with the base, making sure that the tip is completely filled and contains no air bubbles. Adjust the level of the liquid in the buret so that the bottom of the meniscus is at exactly 0.00 mL. Record the initial buret reading (0.00 mL) in the space provided on the report form.

Add 3 drops of phenolphthalein solution to each 125 mL flask containing KHP and water. Place the first (Sample 1) on a piece of white paper under the buret extending the tip of the buret into the flask (see Figure 22.2).

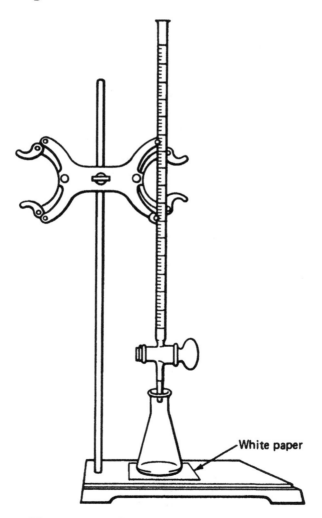

Figure 22.2   Setup with stopcock buret

Titrate the KHP by adding base until the end-point is reached. The titration is conducted by swirling the solution in the flask with the right hand (if you are right handed) while manipulating the stopcock with the left (Figure 22.3). As base is added you will observe a pink color caused by localized high base concentration. Toward the end-point the color flashes throughout the solution, remaining for a longer time. When this occurs, add the base drop by drop until the end-point is reached, as indicated by the first drop of base which causes a faint pink color to remain in the entire solution for at least 30 seconds. Read and record the final buret reading (see Figure 22.5). Refill the buret to the zero mark and repeat the titration with Sample 2. Then, calculate the molarity of the base in each sample. If these molarities differ by more than 0.004, titrate a third sample.

When you are finished with the titrations, empty and rinse the buret at least twice (including the tip) with tap water and once with distilled water. Return the vial with the unused KHP.

Use of the Buret

A buret is a volumetric instrument that is calibrated to deliver a measured volume of solution. The 50 mL buret is calibrated from 0 to 50 mL in 0.1 mL increments and is read to the nearest 0.01 mL. All volumes delivered from the buret should be between the calibration marks. (Do not estimate above the 0 mL mark or below the 50 mL mark.)

1. **Cleaning the Buret.**   The buret must be clean in order to deliver the calibrated volume. Drops of liquid clinging to the sides as the buret is drained are evidence of a dirty buret.

To clean the buret, first rinse it a couple of times with tap water, pouring the water from a beaker. Then scrub it with a detergent solution, using a long-handled buret brush. Rinse the buret several times with tap water and finally with distilled water. Check for cleanliness by draining the distilled water through the tip and observe whether droplets of water remain on the inner walls of the buret.

2. **Using the Buret.**   After draining the distilled water, rinse the buret with two 5 to 10 mL portions of the titrating solution to be used in it. This rinsing is done by holding the buret in a horizontal position and rolling the solution around to wet the entire inner surface. Allow the final rinsing to drain through the tip.

Fill the buret with the solution to slightly above the 0 mL mark and adjust it to 0.00 mL, or some other volume below this mark, by draining the solution through the tip. The buret tip must be completely filled to deliver the volume measured.

To deliver the solution from the buret, turn the stopcock with the forefinger and the thumb of your left hand (if you are right handed) to allow the solution to enter the flask. (See Figure 22.3). This procedure leaves your right hand free to swirl the solution in the flask during the titration. With a little practice you can control the flow so that increments as small as 1 drop of solution can be delivered.

3. **Reading the Buret.**   The smallest calibration mark of a 50 mL buret is 0.1 mL. However, the buret is read to the nearest 0.01 mL by estimating between the calibration marks. When reading the buret be sure your line of sight is level with the bottom of the meniscus in order to avoid parallax errors (see Figure 22.4). The exact bottom of the meniscus may be made more prominent and easier to read by allowing the meniscus to pick up the reflection from a heavy dark line on a piece of paper (see Figure 22.5).

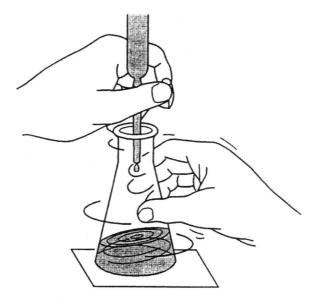

Figure 22.3   Titration technique

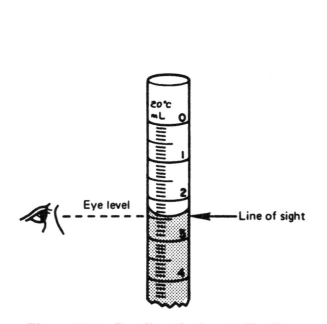

Figure 22.4   Reading the buret. The line
of sight must be level with the bottom of
the meniscus to avoid parallax.

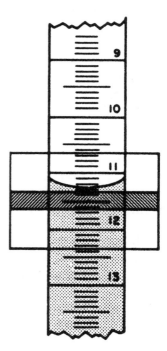

Figure 22.5   Reading the meniscus.
A heavy dark line brought to within one
division of the meniscus will make the
meniscus more prominent and easier to
read. The volume reading is 11.28 mL.

REPORT FOR EXPERIMENT 22

Neutralization – Titration I

Data Table

	Sample 1	Sample 2	Sample 3 (if needed)
Mass of flask and KHP			
Mass of empty flask			
Mass of KHP			
Final buret reading			
Initial buret reading			
Volume of base used			

CALCULATIONS: In the spaces below show calculation setups **for Sample 1 only.** Show answers for both samples in the boxes. Remember to use the proper number of significant figures in all calculations. (The number 0.005 has only one significant figure.)

	Sample 1	Sample 2	Sample 3 (if needed)
1. Moles of acid (KHP, Molar mass = 204.2)			
2. Moles of base used to neutralize (react with) the above number of moles of acid			
3. Molarity of base (NaOH)			

4. Average molarity of base   _____

5. Unknown base number   _____

QUESTIONS AND PROBLEMS

1. If you had added 50 mL of water to a sample of KHP instead of 30 mL, would the titration of that sample then have required more, less, or the same amount of base? Explain.

2. A student weighed out 1.106 g of KHP How many moles was that?

_____ mol

3. A titration required 18.38 mL of 0.1574 M NaOH solution. How many moles of NaOH were in this volume?

_____ mol

4. A student weighed a sample of KHP and found it weighed 1.276 g. Titration of this KHP required 19.84 mL of base (NaOH). Calculate the molarity of the base.

_____ M

5. Forgetful Freddy weighed his KHP sample, but forgot to bring his report sheet along, so he recorded the mass of KHP on a paper towel. During his titration, which required 18.46 mL of base, he spilled some base on his hands. He remembered to wash his hands, but forgot about the data on the towel, and used it to dry his hands. When he went to calculate the molarity of his base, Freddy discovered that he didn't have the mass of his KHP. His kindhearted instructor told Freddy that his base was 0.2987 M. Calculate the mass of Freddy's KHP sample.

_____ g

6. What mass of solid NaOH would be needed to make 645 mL of Freddy's NaOH solution?

_____ g

EXPERIMENT 23

Neutralization – Titration II

MATERIALS AND EQUIPMENT

Solutions: Acid of unknown molarity, standard base solution (NaOH), vinegar, phenolphthalein indicator. Suction bulb, buret, buret brush, buret clamp, 10 mL volumetric pipet. Wash bottle for distilled water.

DISCUSSION

This experiment may follow Experiment 22 or it may be completed independently of Experiment 22. In either case the discussion section of Experiment 22 supplements the following discussion.

The reaction of an acid and a base to form water and a salt is known as **neutralization.** Hydrochloric acid and sodium hydroxide, for example, react to form sodium chloride and water.

$$HCl(aq) + NaOH(aq) \longrightarrow H_2O(l) + NaCl(aq)$$

The ionic reaction in neutralizations of this type is that of hydrogen (or hydronium) ion reacting with hydroxide ion to form water.

$$H^+(aq) + OH^-(aq) \longrightarrow H_2O(l) \quad or \quad H_3O^+(aq) + OH^-(aq) \longrightarrow 2\,H_2O(l)$$

A monoprotic acid—i.e., an acid having one ionizable hydrogen atom per molecule—reacts with sodium hydroxide (or any other monohydroxy base) on a 1:1 mole basis. This fact is often utilized in determining the concentrations of solutions of acids by titration.

Titration is the process of measuring the volume of one reagent to react with a measured volume or mass of another reagent. In this experiment an acid solution of unknown concentration is titrated with a base solution of known concentration, Phenolphthalein is used as an indicator. This substance is colorless in acid solution, but changes to pink when the solution becomes slightly basic or alkaline. The change of color, caused by a single drop of the base solution in excess over that required to neutralize the acid, marks the **end-point** of the titration.

Molarity (M) is the concentration of a solution expressed in terms of moles of solute per liter of solution.

$$Molarity = \frac{moles}{liter}$$

Thus a solution containing 1.00 mole of solute in 1.00 liter of solution is 1.00 molar (1.00 M). If only 0.155 mole is present in 1.00 liter of solution, it is 0.155 M, etc. To determine the molarity of any quantity it is only necessary to divide the total number of moles of solute present in the solution by the volume (in liters).

To determine the number of moles of solute present in a known volume of solution, multiply the volume in liters by the molarity.

$$\text{Moles} = (\text{liters})(\text{molarity}) = (\text{liters})\left(\frac{\text{moles}}{\text{liter}}\right)$$

For titrations involving monoprotic acids and monohydroxy bases (one hydroxide ion per formula unit), the number of moles of acid is identical to the number of moles of base required to neutralize the acid. In this experiment we measure the volume of base of known molarity required to neutralize a measured volume of acid of unknown molarity. The molarity of the acid can then be calculated.

$$\text{Moles base} = (\text{liters})(\text{molarity}) = (\text{liters base})\left(\frac{\text{moles base}}{\text{liters}}\right)$$

$$\text{Moles acid} = (\text{moles base})\left(\frac{1 \text{ mole acid}}{1 \text{ mole base}}\right)$$

$$\text{Molarity of acid} = \frac{\text{moles acid}}{\text{liters acid}}$$

In order to determine the molarity of an acid solution, it is not actually necessary to know what the acid is—only whether it is monoprotic, diprotic, or triprotic. The calculations in this experiment are based on the assumption that the acid in the unknown is monoprotic.

If the molarity and the formula of the solute are known, the concentration in grams of solute per liter of the solution may be calculated by multiplying by the molar mass.

$$(\text{Molarity})(\text{molar mass}) = \left(\frac{\text{moles}}{\text{liter}}\right)\left(\frac{\text{grams}}{\text{mole}}\right) = \frac{\text{grams}}{\text{liter}}$$

In determining the acid content of commercial vinegar, it is customary to treat the vinegar as a dilute solution of acetic acid, $HC_2H_3O_2$. The acetic acid concentration of the vinegar may be calculated as grams of acetic acid per liter or as percent acid by mass. If the acetic acid content is to be expressed on a mass percent basis, the density of the vinegar must also be known.

PROCEDURE

Wear protective glasses.

 Do not pipet by mouth.

 Dispose of all solutions in the sink. Flush with water.

A. Molarity of an Unknown Acid

Obtain a sample of acid of unknown molarity in a clean, dry 125 mL Erlenmeyer flask as directed by your instructor.

With a volumetric pipet, transfer a 10.00 mL sample of the acid to a clean, but not necessarily dry, Erlenmeyer flask. See "Use of the Pipet," on the following page, for instructions on cleaning and using the pipet. Pipet a duplicate 10.00 mL sample into a second flask. (If pipets are not available, a buret which has been carefully cleaned and rinsed may be used to measure the acid samples.)

You will need about 150 mL of base of known molarity (standard solution). Your instructor will give you the exact molarity of the base solution that you used in Experiment 22 or you may be given another sodium hydroxide solution of known molarity. Record the exact molarity of this solution. Keep the flask containing the base stoppered when not in use.

Clean and set up a buret. See "Use of the Buret," in Experiment 22, for instructions on cleaning and using the buret.

Rinse the buret with two 5 to 10 mL portions of the base, running the second rinsing through the buret tip. Discard the rinsings in the sink. Fill the buret with the base, making sure that the tip is completely filled and contains no air bubbles. Adjust the level of the liquid in the buret so that the bottom of the meniscus is near or exactly at 0.00 mL. Record the initial buret reading in the space provided on the report form.

Add three drops of phenolphthalein solution and about 25 mL of distilled water to the flask containing the 10.00 mL of acid. Place this flask on a piece of white paper under the buret and lower the buret tip into the flask (see Figure 22.2).

Titrate the acid by adding base until the end-point is reached. During the titration swirl the solution in the flask with the right hand (if you are right handed) while manipulating the stopcock with the left. As the base is added you will observe a pink color caused by localized high base concentration. Near the end-point this color flashes throughout the solution, remaining for increasingly longer periods of time. When this occurs, add the base drop by drop until the end-point is reached, as indicated by the first drop of base which causes the entire solution to retain a faint pink color for at least 30 seconds. Record the final buret reading.

Refill the buret with base and adjust the volume to near the zero mark. Titrate the duplicate sample of acid. If the volumes of base used differ by more than 0.20 mL, titrate a third sample. In the calculations, assume that the unknown acid reacts like KHP or HCl (one mole of acid reacts with one mole of base).

B.   Acetic Acid Content of Vinegar

Obtain about 40 mL of vinegar in a clean, dry 50 mL beaker. Record the sample number, if any, of this vinegar.

Titrate duplicate 10.00 mL samples of vinegar using exactly the same procedure outlined in Part A. Remember to rinse the pipet with vinegar before pipeting the vinegar samples.

When you are finished with the titrations, empty the buret and rinse it and the pipet at least twice with tap water and once with distilled water.

Use of the Pipet

A volumetric (transfer) pipet (Figure 23.1) is calibrated to deliver a specified volume of liquid to a precision of about ±0.02 mL in a 10 mL pipet. To achieve this precision, the pipet must be clean and used in a specified manner.

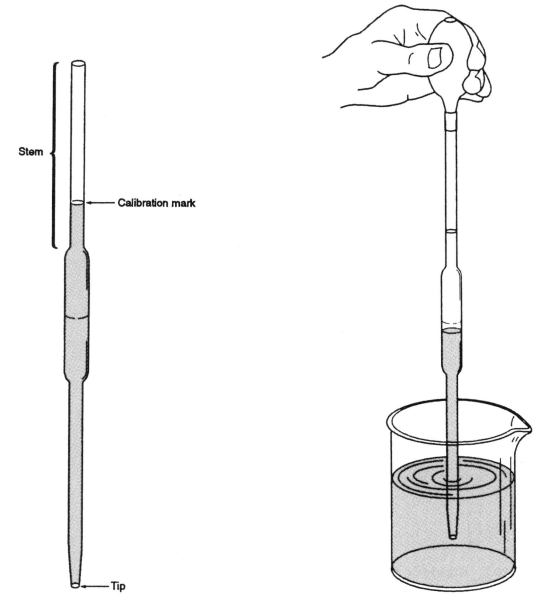

Figure 23.1   A volumetric (transfer) pipet

Figure 23.2   Liquid is drawn into the pipet with a rubber suction bulb. Keep the tip of the pipet below the liquid level during suction.

Liquids are drawn into a pipet by means of a rubber suction bulb (Figure 23.2) or by a rubber tube connected to a water aspirator pump. Suction by mouth has also been used to draw liquids into a pipet, but this is a dangerous practice and is not recommended.

1. **Cleaning the Pipet.**   Use a rubber suction bulb to draw up enough detergent solution to fill about two-thirds of the body or bulb of the pipet. Retain this solution in the pipet by pressing the forefinger tightly against the top of the pipet stem (Figure 23.3). turn the pipet to a nearly horizontal position and gently shake and rotate it until the entire inside surface is wetted. Allow the pipet to drain and rinse it at least three times with tap water and once with distilled water.

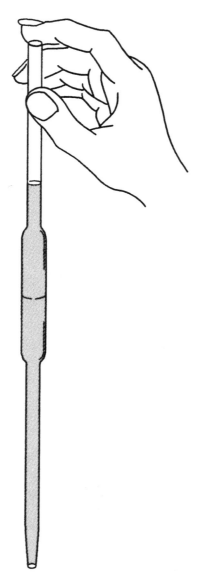

Figure 23.3   Liquid is retained in the pipet by applying pressure with the forefinger to the top of the stem.

Figure 23.4   The pipet is calibrated to deliver the specified volume, leaving a small amount of liquid in the tip.

2. **Using the Pipet.**   Unless the pipet is known to be clean and absolutely dry on the inside, it must be rinsed twice with small portions of the liquid that is to be pipeted. This is done as in the washing procedure described above. These rinses are discarded in order to avoid contamination of the liquid being pipeted. A **pipet** does not need to be rinsed between successive pipettings of the same solution.

To transfer a measured volume of a liquid, collapse a suction bulb by squeezing and place it tightly against the top of a pipet. (Do not try to push the bulb on to the pipet.) Draw the liquid into the pipet until it is filled to about 5 cm above the calibration mark by allowing the bulb to slowly expand. Be careful—do not allow the liquid to get into the bulb. Remove the bulb and quickly place your forefinger over the top of the pipet stem. The liquid will be retained in the pipet if the finger is pressed tightly against the top of the stem. Keeping the pipet in a vertical position, decrease the finger pressure very slightly, and allow the liquid level to drop slowly toward the calibration mark. When the liquid level has almost reached the calibration mark, again increase the finger pressure and stop the liquid when the bottom of the meniscus is exactly on the calibration mark. Touch the tip to the wall of the flask to remove the adhering drop of liquid.

Move the pipet to the flask which is to receive the sample and allow the liquid to drain while holding the pipet in a vertical position. About 10 seconds after the liquid has stopped running from the pipet, touch the tip to the inner wall of the sample flask to remove the drop of liquid adhering to the tip. A small amount of liquid will remain in the tip (Figure 23.4). Do not blow or shake this liquid into the sample; the pipet is calibrated to deliver the volume specified without this small residual.

If you have never used a volumetric pipet, it is advisable to practice by pipetting some samples of distilled water until you have mastered the technique.

NAME ____________________

SECTION ______ DATE ______

REPORT FOR EXPERIMENT 23

INSTRUCTOR________________

Neutralization-Titration II

A. Molarity of an Unknown Acid

Data Table

	Sample 1		**Sample 2**		**Sample 3 (if needed)**	
	Acid*	Base	Acid*	Base	Acid*	Base
Final buret reading						
Initial buret reading						
Volume used						

*If a pipet is used to measure the volume of acid, record only in the space for volume used.

Molarity of base (NaOH) ______________

CALCULATIONS: In the spaces below, show calculation setups for Sample 1 only. Show answers for both samples in the boxes.

	Sample 1	**Sample 2**	**Sample 3 (if needed)**
1. Moles of base (NaOH) (if needed)	______	______	______
2. Moles of acid used to neutralize (react with) the above number of moles of base	______	______	______
3. Molarity of acid	______	______	______

4. Average molarity of acid ______________

5. Unknown acid number ______________

REPORT FOR EXPERIMENT 23 (continued)   NAME _____

B. Acetic Acid Content of Vinegar

Data Table

	Sample 1		Sample 2		Sample 3 (if needed)	
	Vinegar*	Base	Vinegar*	Base	Vinegar*	Base
Final buret reading						
Initial buret reading						
Volume used						

*If a pipet is used to measure the volume of vinegar, record only in the space for volume used.

Molarity of base (NaOH) _____   Vinegar number _____

CALCULATIONS: In the spaces below, show calculation setups for Sample 1 only. Show answers for both samples in the boxes.

	Sample 1	Sample 2	Sample 3 (if needed)

1. Moles of base (NaOH)

2. Moles of acid ($HC_2H_3O_2$) used to neutralize (react with) the above number of moles of base

3. Molarity of acetic acid in the vinegar

4. Average molarity of acetic acid in the vinegar   _____

5. Grams of acetic acid per liter (from average molarity)   _____

6. Mass percent acetic acid in vinegar sample (density of vinegar = 1.005 g/mL)   _____

EXPERIMENT 24

Chemical Equilibrium – Reversible Reactions

MATERIALS AND EQUIPMENT

Solid: ammonium chloride (NH_4Cl). **Solutions:** saturated ammonium chloride, 0.1 M cobalt(II) chloride ($CoCl_2$), 0.1 M iron(III) chloride ($FeCl_3$), concentrated (12 M) hydrochloric acid (HCl), 0.1 M copper(II) sulfate ($CuSO_4$), 6 M ammonium hydroxide (NH_4OH), phenolphthalein, 0.1 M potassium thiocyanate (KSCN), 0.1 M silver nitrate ($AgNO_3$), saturated sodium chloride (NaCl), and dilute (3 M) sulfuric acid (H_2SO_4).

DISCUSSION

In many chemical reactions the reactants are not totally converted to the products because of a reverse reaction; that is, because the products react to form the original reactants. Such reactions are said to be reversible and are indicated by a double arrow ($\rightleftharpoons$) in the equation. The reaction proceeding to the right is called the **forward reaction;** that to the left, the **reverse reaction.** Both reactions occur simultaneously.

Every chemical reaction proceeds at a certain rate or speed. The rate of a reaction is variable and depends on the concentrations of the reactants and the conditions under which the reaction is conducted. When the rate of the forward reaction is equal to the rate of the reverse reaction, a condition of **chemical equilibrium** exists. At equilibrium the products react at the same rate as they are produced. Thus the concentrations of substances in equilibrium do not change, but both reactions, forward and reverse, are still occurring.

The principle of Le Chatelier relates to systems in equilibrium and states that when the conditions of a system in equilibrium are changed the system reacts to counteract the change and reestablish equilibrium. In this experiment we will observe the effect of changing the concentration of one or more substances in a chemical equilibrium. Consider the hypothetical equilibrium system

$$A + B \rightleftharpoons C + D$$

When the concentration of any one of the species in this equilibrium is changed, the equilibrium is disturbed. Changes in the concentrations of all the other substances will occur to establish a new position of equilibrium. For example, when the concentration of B is increased, the rate of the forward reaction increases, the concentration of A decreases, and the concentrations of C and D increase. After a period of time the two rates will become equal and the system will again be in equilibrium. The following statements indicate how the equilibrium will shift when the concentrations of A, B, C, and D are changed.

An increase in the concentration of A or B causes the equilibrium to shift to the right.

An increase in the concentration of C or D causes the equilibrium to shift to the left.

A decrease in the concentration of A or B causes the equilibrium to shift to the left.

A decrease in the concentration of C or D causes the equilibrium to shift to the right.

Evidence of a shift in equilibrium by a change in concentration can easily be observed if one of the substances involved in the equilibrium is colored. The appearance of a precipitate or the change in color of an indicator can sometimes be used to detect a shift in equilibrium.

Net ionic equations for the equilibrium systems to be studied are given below. These equations will be useful for answering the questions in the report form.

A. **Saturated Sodium Chloride Solution**

$$NaCl(s) \underset{}{\overset{H_2O}{\rightleftharpoons}} Na^+(aq) + Cl^-(aq)$$

B. **Saturated Ammonium Chloride Solution**

$$NH_4Cl(s) \underset{}{\overset{H_2O}{\rightleftharpoons}} NH_4^+(aq) + Cl^-(aq)$$

C. **Iron(III) Chloride plus Potassium Thiocyanate**

$$Fe^{3+}(aq) + SCN^-(aq) \rightleftharpoons Fe(SCN)^{2+}(aq)$$
    Pale   Colorless   Red
    yellow

D. **Copper(II) Sulfate Solution with Ammonia**

$$Cu(H_2O)_4^{2+}(aq) + 4\,NH_3(aq) \rightleftharpoons Cu(OH)_2(s) \rightleftharpoons [Cu(NH_3)_4]^{2+}(aq) + 4\,H_2O$$
      light blue   blue   deep blue/purple
         clear   cloudy   cloudy

E. **Cobalt(II) Chloride Solution**

The equilibrium involves the following ions in solutions:

$$Co(H_2O)_6{}^{2+}(aq) + 4\,Cl^-(aq) \rightleftharpoons CoCl_4{}^{2-}(aq) + 6\,H_2O(l)$$
    Pink   Blue

F. **Ammonia Solution**

$$NH_3(aq) + H_2O(l) \rightleftharpoons NH_4^+(aq) + OH^-(aq)$$

PROCEDURE

Wear protective glasses.

NOTE: Record observed evidence of equilibrium shifts as each experiment is done.

A.   Saturated Sodium Chloride Solution

Add a few drops of conc. hydrochloric acid to 2 to 3 mL of saturated sodium chloride solution in a test tube, and note the results.

B.   Saturated Ammonium Chloride Solution

Repeat Part A, using saturated ammonium chloride solution instead of sodium chloride solution.

 Dispose of the solutions in A and B in the sink and flush with water.

C.   Iron(III) Chloride plus Potassium Thiocyanate

Prepare a stock solution to be tested by adding 2 mL each of 0.1 M iron(III) chloride and 0.1 M potassium thiocyanate solutions to 100 mL of distilled water and mix. Pour about 5 mL of this stock solution into each of four test tubes.

1. Use the first tube as a control for color comparison.

2. Add about 1 mL of 0.1 M iron(III) chloride solution to the second tube and observe the color change.

3. Add about 1 mL of 0.1 M potassium thiocyanate solution to the third tube and observe the color change.

4. Add 0.1 M silver nitrate solution dropwise (less than 1 mL) to the fourth tube until almost all the color is discharged. The white precipitate formed consists of both AgCl and AgSCN. Pour about half the contents (including the precipitate) into another tube. Add 0.1 M potassium thiocyanate solution dropwise (1 to 2 mL) to one tube and 0.1 M iron(III) chloride solution (1 to 2 mL) to the other. Observe the results.

 Dispose of the contents in tubes C.1–3 and the unused stock solutions in the sink and flush with water. Dispose of the contents of both C.4 tubes in the "heavy metals" waste container.

D.   Copper (II) Sulfate Solution with Ammonia

Pour 2 mL of 0.1 M copper (II) sulfate into each of two test tubes. Add 6 M $NH_3(aq)$ (NH_4OH) dropwise (shake well after each drop is added) to one of the copper(II) sulfate tubes. When there is a definite color or appearance change, note the change on the report form. Use the second test tube for comparison. Continue to add the $NH_3(aq)$ until there is another color or appearance change. Note the changes on the report form.

Now, add 3 M H_2SO_4 dropwise to the solution until the original color is restored. Again, use the second tube for comparison.

 Dispose of the contents of both test tubes in the "heavy metals" waste container provided.

E.   Cobalt(II) Chloride Solution

Place about 2 mL (no more) of 0.1 M cobalt(II) chloride solution into each of three test tubes.

    1. To one tube add about 3 mL of conc. hydrochloric acid dropwise and note the result. Now add water dropwise to the solution until the original color (reverse reaction) is evident.

    2. To the second tube add about 1.5 g of solid ammonium chloride and shake to make a saturated salt solution. Compare the color with the solution in the third tube (control). Place the second and third tubes (unstoppered) in a beaker of boiling water, shake occasionally, and note the results. Cool both tubes under tap water until the original color (reverse reaction) is evident.

 Dispose of these solutions in the "heavy metals" waste container.

F.   Ammonia Solution

Prepare an ammonia stock solution by adding 10 drops of 6 M ammonium hydroxide and 3 drops of phenolphthalein to 100 mL of tap water and mix. Pour about 5 mL of this stock solution into each of two test tubes.

    1. Dissolve a very small amount of solid ammonium chloride in the stock solution in the first tube and observe the result.

    2. Add a few drops of dil. (6 M) hydrochloric acid to the stock solution in the second tube. Mix and observe the result.

 Dispose of these solutions and the rest of the ammonia stock solution in the sink and flush with water.

REPORT FOR EXPERIMENT 24

Chemical Equilibrium – Reversible Reactions

Refer to equilibrium equations in the discussion when answering these questions.

A. Saturated Sodium Chloride

1. What is the evidence for a shift in equilibrium?

2. Which ion caused the equilibrium to shift?   _____

3. In which direction did the equilibrium shift?   _____

4. If solid sodium hydroxide were added to neutralize the hydrochloric acid, would this reverse the reaction and cause the precipitated sodium chloride to redissolve? Explain.

B. Saturated Ammonium Chloride

1. What is the evidence for a shift in equilibrium?

2. In which direction did the equilibrium shift?   _____

3. Which ion caused the equilibrium to shift?   _____

C. Iron(III) Chloride plus Potassium Thiocyanate

1. What is the evidence for a shift in equilibrium when iron(III) chloride is added to the stock solution?

2. What is the evidence for a shift in equilibrium when potassium thiocyanate is added to the stock solution?

3. (a) What is the evidence for a shift in equilibrium when silver nitrate is added to the stock solution? (The formation of a precipitate is not the evidence since the precipitate is not one of the substances in the equilibrium.)

 (b) The change in concentration of which ion in the equilibrium caused this equilibrium shift?

_____

 (c) Write a net ionic equation to illustrate how this concentration change occurred.

 (d) When the mixture in C.4 was divided and further tested, what evidence showed that the mixture still contained Fe^{3+} ions in solution?

D. Copper(II) Sulfate Solution with Ammonia

1. What was the evidence for the first shift in equilibrium when the $NH_3(aq)$ was added dropwise to the Cu^{2+} solution?

2. (a) Explain how adding more $NH_3(aq)$ caused the equilibria to shift again.

 (b) What did you observe in the Cu^{2+} system to indicate that the shift had occured?

3. (a) Explain how 3 M sulfuric acid caused the equilibria to shift back again?

 (b) What did you observe to indicate that the reaction shifted to the left?

E. Cobalt(II) Chloride Solution

1. What was the evidence for a shift in equilibrium when conc. hydrochloric acid was added to the cobalt chloride solution?

2. (a) Write the equilibrium equation for this system.

   (b) State whether the concentration of each of the following substances was increased, decreased, or unaffected when the conc. hydrochloric acid was added to cobalt chloride solution.

   $Co(H_2O)_6^{2+}$ _____, Cl^- _____, $CoCl_4^{2-}$ _____

3. (a) What did you observe when ammonium chloride was added to cobalt chloride solution?

   (b) What did you observe when this mixture was heated?

   (c) Explain why heating the mixture caused the equilibrium to shift.

   (d) What did you observe when the mixture was cooled?

   (e) Explain why cooling the mixture caused the equilibrium to shift.

F. Ammonia Solution

1. What is the evidence for a shift in equilibrium when ammonium chloride was added to the stock solution?

2. Explain, in terms of the equilibrium, the results observed when hydrochloric acid was added to the stock solution.

3. State whether the concentration of each of the following was increased, decreased, or was unaffected when dilute hydrochloric acid was added to the ammonia stock solution:

NH_3 _____, NH_4^+ _____, OH^- _____,   Pink color _____

4. (a) In which direction would the equilibrium shift if sodium hydroxide were added to the ammonia stock solution?

   (b) Would the sodium hydroxide tend to decrease the color intensity? Explain.

5. Would boiling the ammonia solution have any effect on the equilibrium? Explain.

APPENDIX 1

Suggested List of Equipment

Equipment for Student Lockers

1. 5 Beakers: 50, 100, 150, 250, 400 mL
2. 1 Burner, Tirrill (optional)
3. 1 Ceramfab pad
4. 1 Clay triangle
5. 2 Crucibles, size 0
6. 2 Crucible covers, size F
7. 1 Crucible tongs
8. 1 Evaporating dish, size 1
9. 1 File, triangular
10. 1 Filter paper (box)
11. 2 Flasks, Erlenmeyer, 125 mL
12. 2 Flasks, Erlenmeyer, 250 mL
13. 1 Flask, florence, 500 mL
14. 5 Glass plates, 3 × 3 in.
15. 1 Graduated cylinder, 10 mL
16. 1 Graduated cylinder, 50 mL
17. 2 Litmus paper (vials), red and blue
18. 2 Medicine droppers/disposable pipets
19. 1 Pipet, volumetric, 10 mL
20. 8 Rubber stoppers: 3 No. 1, solid;
    1 No. 1, 1-hole; 1 No. 4, 1-hole;
    1 No. 4, 2-hole; 1 No. 5, solid;
    1 No. 6, 2-hole
21. 2 Rubber tubing (about 25 cm), 3/16 in. diameter
22. 1 Screw clamp
23. 1 Spatula
24. 1 Sponge
25. 12 Test tubes, 18 × 150 mm (or culture tubes)
26. 1 Test tube, ignition, 25 × 200 mm
27. 1 Test tube brush
28. 1 Test tube holder, wire
29. 1 Test tube rack
30. 1 Thermometer, 110°C
31. 1 Thistle top, plastic
32. 1 Utility clamp (single buret clamp)
33. 1 Wash bottle (plastic)
34. 2 Watch glasses, 4 in.
35. 5 Wide-mouth bottles, 8 oz.
36. 1 Wing top
37. 1 Wire gauze

Auxillary Equipment Not Supplied in Student Lockers

1. Aluminum foil (7 × 7 cm)
2. Balances
3. Beakers, 600 mL
4. Blender
5. Boyle's law apparatus
6. Büchner funnels, suction flasks, and suction rubber tubing
7. Burets, 25 or 50 mL
8. Buret clamps
9. Burners, Tirrill (if not individually supplied)
10. Capillary Melting point tubes (sealed at one end)
11. Centrifuges
12. Centrifuge tubes
13. Cheese cloth
14. Chromatography columns (polypropylene from Kontes)
15. Deflagration spoons
16. Erlenmeyer flasks, 500 mL
17. Filter paper, Whatman #1 (14 × 14 cm)
18. Filter paper for Büchner funnel
19. Glass rod, 5 or 6 mm
20. Glass tubing, 6 mm
21. Glass wool (pyrex)
22. Glass writing markers
23. Gloves, plastic; small and medium
24. Hair dryers
25. Magnetic stirrers with bars
26. Metric rulers
27. Oil baths
28. pH meters
29. Pipets, graduated, 1 mL, 5 mL, and 10 mL
30. Pipets, micro
31. Pipets, Pasteur
32. Pipets, volumetric; 2 mL and 3 mL
33. Pneumatic troughs
34. Protective rubber gloves
35. Reflux and distillation equipment
    100 mL or 200 mL round-bottom distilling flasks
    Distillation take-off heads
    Condensers
    200° or 250° thermometers
    250 mL separatory funnels
36. Ring stands
37. Ring supports, 4 to 5 in. diameter
38. Rubber bands cut from 3/16 inch rubber tubing
39. Spectrophotometers
40. Spray applicators
41. Styrofoam cups, 6 ounce
42. Suction bulbs for pipets
43. Wire stirrers for oil and water baths
44. Four inch cardboard square with a hole for a thermometer
45. See Appendix 3 for special equipment needed for some experiments.
46. See Exp. 8 for special equipment needed.

APPENDIX 2

List of Reagents Required and Preparation of Solutions

Solids

Acetamide, C_2H_5NO

Aluminum foil

Ammonium chloride, NH_4Cl

Barium chloride, $BaCl_2 \cdot 2\,H_2O$

Barium sulfate, $BaSO_4$

Benzoic acid, C_6H_5COOH

Benzophenone, $C_6H_5-CO-C_6H_5$

Benzoyl peroxide, $(C_6H_5COO)_2$

Boiling chips

Candles

Calcium carbide, CaC_2 (small lumps)

Calcium hydroxide, $Ca(OH)_2$

Calcium oxide, CaO

Cholesterol, $C_{27}H_{45}OH$

trans-Cinnamic acid, $C_9H_8O_2$

Copper (II) acetate, $Cu(C_2H_3O_2) \cdot H_2O$, (for Barfoed reagent)

Cobalt chloride paper

Copper strips, Cu

Copper wire, #18, Cu

Copper(II) sulfate pentahydrate, $CuSO_4 \cdot 5\,H_2O$

Cotton

Digitonin, $C_{56}H_{92}O_{29}$

Diphenylacetic acid, $C_{14}H_{12}O_2$

Diphenylacetic acid-cholesterol, 50:50

Dipotassium phosphate, K_2HPO_4, (for phosphate buffer)

Food coloring, red and green paste

Glass wool, pyrex

Glucose, $C_6H_{12}O_6$

Glycine, $C_2H_5NO_2$

Ice

Ice cubes, dark blue

Iodine, I_2

Iron wire (20-24 gauge), Fe

Lead strips, Pb

Lead(II) iodide, PbI_2

Magnesium strips, Mg

Magnesium oxide, MgO

Magnesium sulfate, anhydrous, $MgSO_4$

Magnesium sulfate, $MgSO_4 \cdot 7H_2O$

Manganese dioxide, MnO_2

Marble chips, $CaCO_3$

Marbles, about 20 mm diameter

Menthol, $C_{10}H_{20}O$

Methylene blue, powder

1-Naphthol, (α-naphthol) $C_{10}H_8O$

Ninhydrin, $C_9H_6O_4$

p-Nitroaniline, $C_6H_6N_2O_2$

1-Nitroso-2-naphthol, $C_{10}H_7NO_2$

Orcinol, (3, 5-dihydroxytoluene) $C_7H_8O_2$, (for Bial reagent)

pH indicator paper, 1–14

Phenol, C_6H_5OH

Potassium bicarbonate, $KHCO_3$

Potassium bisulfate, $KHSO_4$

Potassium chlorate, C.P, $KClO_3$

Potassium chloride, C.P, KCl

Potassium hydrogen phthalate, $KHC_8H_4O_4$

Potassium hydroxide, KOH; for phosphate buffer solution

Potato (fresh)

Resorcinol, $C_6H_6O_2$ (for Seliwanoff reagent)

Sand paper or emery cloth

Salicylic acid, $C_6H_4(COOH)(OH)$

Sodium, Na

Sodium bicarbonate, $NaHCO_3$

Sodium carbonate, anhydrous; Na_2CO_3

Sodium chloride (coarse crystals), NaCl

Sodium chloride (fine crystals), NaCl

Sodium Citrate, $C_6H_5Na_3O_2$

Sodium nitrate, $NaNO_3$

Sodium nitrite, $NaNO_2$

Sodium peroxide, Na_2O_2

Sodium potassium tartrate, $NaKC_4H_4O_6$ (used in copper reagent)

Sodium sulfate, anhydrous, Na_2SO_4

Sodium sulfite, Na_2SO_3

Starch, $(C_6H_{10}O_5)_n$

Stearic acid, $CH_3(CH_2)_{16}COOH$

Steel wool, Fe (Grade 0 or 1)

Strontium chloride, $SrCl_2 \cdot 6\ H_2O$

Sucrose, $C_{12}H_{22}O_{11}$

Sulfur, S

Tin (II) chloride, $SnCl_2 \cdot 6H_2O$

Tyrosine, $C_9H_{11}NO_3$

Urea, $(NH_2)_2CO$

Urea-trans-cinnamic acid, 50:50

Vegetable shortening

Wood splints

Xylose, $C_5H_{10}O_5$

Zinc, mossy, Zn

Zinc strips, Zn (0.01 inch thick)

Zinc sulfate, $ZnSO_4 \cdot 7\ H_2O$

Pure Liquids/Commercial Mixtures

Acetic acid (glacial), CH_3COOH

Acetic anhydride, $(CH_3CO)_2O$

Acetone, CH_3COCH_3

Aniline, C_6H_7N

Benzylamine, C_7H_9N

Bromine, Br_2

n-Butyl alcohol (1-butanol), C_4H_9OH

Chloroform, $CHCl_3$

Cyclohexane, C_6H_{12}

Decane, $C_{10}H_{22}$

1,6-Diaminohexane, $C_6H_{16}N_2$

Diethylamine, $C_4H_{11}N$

Ethyl alcohol (ethanol), 95%, C_2H_5OH

Ethyl alcohol, denatured anhydrous

Formaldehyde, formalin, 40% CH_2O solution

Glycerol, $C_3H_5(OH)_3$

Heptane (or low boiling petroleum ether), C_7H_{16}

Hexane, C_6H_{14}

n-Hexylamine, $C_6H_{13}NH_2$

Isoamyl alcohol (3-methyl-1-butanol), $C_5H_{11}OH$

Isopropyl alcohol (2-propanol) C_3H_7OH

Kerosene (alkene free)

Liquid detergent

Methyl alcohol (methanol), CH_3OH

Methyl methacrylate, $CH_2{=}CH(CH_3)COOCH_3$

Mineral oil, (for melting point bath)

Oleic acid, $CH_3(CH_2)_7CH{=}CH(CH_2)_7COOH$

Pentene (amylene), C_5H_{10}

Phosphoric acid, 85% H_3PO_4

Pyridine, C_5H_5N

Red wine

Sulfuric acid, conc., H_2SO_4

Toluene, C_7H_8

1,1,1-Trichloroethane, CCl_3CH_3

Vegetable oils (corn, cottonseed, peanut, soybean, etc.)

Appendix 2 (continued)

Solutions

All solutions, except where otherwise directed, are prepared by dissolving the designated quantity of solute in distilled water and diluting to 1 liter.

Acetic acid, concentrated (glacial), concentrated reagent $HC_2H_3O_2$

Acetic acid, dilute, 6 M; 350 mL concentrated $HC_2H_3O_2$/liter

Acetic acid, 10% solution; 100 mL CH_3COOH + 900 mL H_2O

Acetic acid-1-butanol-water (1:3:1 by volume); 200 mL CH_3COOH + 600 mL C_4H_9OH/liter

Adipoyl chloride, 0.4 M in cyclohexane; 18.3 g adipoyl chloride/250 mL cyclohexane

Alanine, 0.2 M; 1.78 g alanine/100 mL

Alanine·HCl, 0.1 M; 1.26 g alanine·HCl/100 mL

Alanine-aspartic acid-leucine-lysine solution (each 0.2 M); 1.78 g alanine + 2.66 g aspartic acid + 2.62 g leucine + 2.92 g lysine/100 mL

Albumin, 2%; 20 g albumin/liter (Make slurry with about 50 mL water, then add additional water slowly while stirring.)

Aluminum chloride, 0.10 M; 24.1 g $AlCl_3$·6 H_2O/liter

Ammonium chloride, 0.1 M; 5.4 g NH_4Cl/liter

Ammonium chloride, saturated; 410 g NH_4Cl/liter

Ammonium hydroxide, concentrated; concentrated reagent, NH_4OH

Ammonium hydroxide, dilute, 6 M; 400 mL concentrated/liter, NH_4OH

Arabinose, 1%; 10 g arabinose/liter

Arginine-tyrosine solution (each 0.1 %); 100 mg arginine + 100 mg tyrosine/100 mL pH 6.0 phosphate buffer

Arsenomolybdate reagent; Nelson's arsenomolybdate reagent is commercially available from Sigma Chemical Co., St. Louis, Missouri

Aspartic acid, 0.2 M; 2.66 g aspartic acid/100 mL

Barfoed reagent; dissolve 13.3 g $Cu(C_2H_3O_2)_2$·H_2O in 200 mL H_2O. (Filter if necessary), add 1.8 mL $HC_2H_3O_2$ (glacial). Copper(II) acetate is slow to dissolve.

Barium chloride, 0.10 M; 24.4 g $BaCl_2$·2 H_2O/liter

Barium hydroxide, saturated; 10 g $Ba(OH)_2$·8 H_2O/100 mL

Barium hydroxide, 0.2 M; 15.8 g $Ba(OH)_2$·8 H_2O/250 mL

Benedict reagent; dissolve 86.5 g sodium citrate and 50 g anhydrous Na_2CO_3 in 400 mL water with heating. Dissolve 8.65 g $CuSO_4$·5 H_2O in 50 mL water. Mix these two solutions slowly and add water to produce 500 mL of solution.

Bial reagent; dissolve 1.5 g orcinol (3, 5-dihydroxytoluene) in 500 mL conc. HCl and add 1.5 mL of 10% aqueous $FeCl_3$

Bleach, 10% NaOCl solution

Blood, sheep (or any mammalian non-human blood) Should be fresh. (Ward's Scientific or Carolina Biological Supply, or local source).

Bromine in 1,1,1-trichloroethane, 5% solution; 2.5 mL Br_2 plus 100 mL CCl_3CH_3

Buffer solution, standard pH 4.0, 7.0, 10.0; commercially available

Calcium chloride, 0.1 M; 14.7 g $CaCl_2 \cdot 2\ H_2O$/liter

Chlorine water; dilute 150 mL of 5.25% NaOCl (household bleach) to 1 liter. Add 15 mL concentrated HCl and mix gently.

Cholesterol standard solution; $C_{27}H_{45}OH$ (dissolve 120 mg cholesterol in 60 mL isopropyl alcohol)

Cobalt (II) chloride, 0.1 M; 23.8 g $CoCl_2 \cdot 6\ H_2O$/liter

Copper (II) nitrate, 0.1 M; 24.2 g $Cu(NO_3)_2 \cdot 3\ H_2O$/liter

Copper reagent; dissolve 24 g of anhydrous Na_2CO_3, 16 g of sodium potassium tartrate, 4 g of $CuSO_4 \cdot 5\ H_2O$, and 180 g of anhydrous Na_2SO_4 in water and dilute to 1 liter.

Copper(II) sulfate, 0.1 M; 25.0 g $CuSO_4 \cdot 5\ H_2O$/liter; or dilute 0.2 M with an equal volume of water

Copper(II) sulfate, 0.2 M; 50.0 g $CuSO_4 \cdot 5\ H_2O$/liter

Copper (II) sulfate, 1%; 1 g $CuSO_4 \cdot 5\ H_2O$ + 99 mL H_2O

Cysteine $\cdot$ HCl, 0.10 M; 1.56 g cysteine $\cdot$ HCl/100 mL

1,6-Diaminohexane (Hexamethylenediamine), 0.40 M in 0.40 M NaOH; dissolve 11.6 g $(CH_2)_6(NH_2)_2$/250 mL 0.4 M NaOH

Digitonin solution; dissolve 1.0 g digitonin in 50 mL ethanol

Dowex-50 slurry; The resin must be in the H^+ form. Newly purchased resin or used resin is washed sequentially with deionized water, acetone (use only for the new resin), 1 M NaOH, deionized water, 1 M HCl, and deionized water. The washed resin is suspended in the pH 6 phosphate buffer two or three times or until the slurry has a pH of 6. Store the slurry in the cold.

Ethanol-Acetone (1:1 by volume); 500 mL CH_3CH_2OH + 500 mL CH_3COCH_3

Ethanol, denatured, CH_3CH_2OH

Ethanol/water, 500 mL CH_3CH_2OH + 500 mL H_2O

Food colors, blue, green, and yellow; commercially available products

Formaldehyde, 10% solution; 25 mL formalin (40% CH_2O) plus 75 mL H_2O

Fructose, 1% solution; 1.0 g fructose/100 mL

Fruit juices; orange, lemon, lime, grapefruit, apple, etc. (fresh if available)

Gelatin, 2% solution; 10 g gelatin/500 mL (Dissolves slowly)

Glucose, 0.020 M; 3.6 g $C_6H_{12}O_6$/liter

Glucose, 1% solution; 5 g $C_6H_{12}O_6$/500 mL H_2O

Glucose, 10% solution; 10 g $C_6H_{12}O_6$ plus 90 mL H_2O

Glucose, standard solutions; made up to contain 2.0, 5.0, 8.0, 12.0, 15.0, and 18 mg glucose/100 mL solution

Glutamic acid·HCl, 0.10 M; 1.84 g glutamic acid·HCl/100 mL

Glycine·HCl, 0.10 M; 1.40 g glycine·HCl/100 mL

Glycine, 1% solution; 1.0 g glycine/100 mL

Histidine·HCl, 0.10 M; 2.10 g histidine·HCl/100 mL

Hydrochloric acid, concentrated, concentrated reagent, HCl

Hydrochloric acid, 0.020 M, 6.7 mL of 3.0 M HCL/liter

Hydrochloric acid, 1.0 M; 86 mL conc. HCL/liter

Hydrochloric acid, dilute, 3 M; 250 mL concentrated HCl/liter

Hydrochloric acid, dilute, 6 M; 500 mL concentrated HCl/liter

Hydrochloric acid, 0.1 M; 8.33 mL concentrated acid HCl/liter; (or dilute 10 mL of 6 M HCl to 600 mL)

Hydrochloric acid, 0.01 M; 0.83 mL concentrated acid HCl/liter; (or dilute 10 mL of 0.1 M HCl to 100 mL)

Hydrochloric acid, 0.001 M; 0.083 mL concentrated acid HCl/liter; (or dilute 10 mL 0.1 M to 1000 mL)

Hydrogen peroxide, 3%; reagent solution or 100 mL 30% H_2O_2/liter

Hydrogen peroxide, 6%; 200 mL 30% H_2O_2/liter; store cold (handle 30% with gloves)

Hydrogen peroxide, 9%; 300 mL 30% H_2O_2/liter; store cold

Hydrogen peroxide, 30% H_2O_2 (for dilution); store cold (handle with gloves)

Iodine, 0.020 M in KI; 1.5 g KI per 100 mL water, add 0.51 g I_2

Iodine in potassium iodide, 1%; 10 g I_2 + 20 g KI/liter (Dissolve I_2 and KI in about 50 mL H_2O, then dilute to 1 liter)

Iodine water, saturated; 5 g I_2/liter

Iron (III) chloride, 0.1 M; 27.1 g $FeCl_3$·6 H_2O + 5 mL concentrated HCl/liter

Iron reagent; 2.5 g $FeCl_3$·6 H_2O/100 mL phosphoric acid

Isopropyl alcohol-water (2:1 by volume); 667 mL $CH_3CH(OH)CH_3$/liter

Lead (II) acetate, 0.1 M; 3.25 g $Pb(C_2H_3O_2)_2$/100 mL

Lead (II) nitrate, 0.10 M; 33.1 g $Pb(NO_3)_2$/liter

Leucine, 0.2 M; 2.62 g leucine/100 mL

Lysine, 0.2 M; 2.92 g lysine/100 mL

Lysine·HCl, 0.1 M; 1.83 g lysine·HCl/100 mL

Magnesium sulfate, 0.1 M; 24.6 g $MgSO_4$·7 H_2O/liter

Maltose, 1% solution; 5.0 g maltose/500 mL

Milk, fat free (skim)

Molisch reagent; dissolve 2.5 g α-naphthol in 50 mL 95% C_2H_5OH

Nickel nitrate, 0.1 M; 29.1 g $Ni(NO_3)_2 \cdot 6\ H_2O$/liter

Ninhydrin, 0.3%; 1.5 g ninhydrin/500 mL acetone

Ninhydrin, 0.2%; dissolve 0.2 g of ninhydrin in 100 mL of 1-butanol which is saturated with water

Nitric acid, concentrated; concentrated reagent, HNO_3

Nitric acid, dilute, 3 M; 188 mL concentrated HNO_3/liter

Nitric acid, dilute, 6 M; 375 mL concentrated HNO_3/liter

1-Nitroso-2-naphthol, 0.1 % in acetone, $C_{10}H_7NO_2$; dissolve 0.17 g in 100 mL acetone

Phenol, 1% solution; 5.0 g C_6H_5OH/500 mL

Phenolphthalein, 0.2% solution; dissolve 2 g phenolphthalein in 600 mL ethanol (95%) and dilute with water to 1 liter

Phosphate buffer, 0.2 M; 34.8 g K_2HPO_4/liter and adjust pH to 6.0 using a pH meter and dilute H_3PO_4 or KOH solution

Phosphoric acid, 85% reagent, H_3PO_4

Phosphoric acid, dilute, 3 M; 201 mL 85% H_3PO_4 solution/liter

Potassium chloride, saturated; 390 g KCl/liter

Potassium nitrate, 0.1 M; 10.1 g KNO_3/liter

Potassium permanganate, 0.1 M; 15.8 g $KMnO_4$/liter

Potassium permanganate, 0.002 M; 0.16 g $KMnO_4$/500 mL H_2O

Potassium thiocyanate, 0.1 M; 9.7 g KSCN/liter

Seliwanoff reagent; dissolve 0.50 g resorcinol in 1000 mL 4 M HCl (333 mL conc. HCl diluted to 1000 mL)

Silver nitrate, 0.10 M; 17.0 g $AgNO_3$/liter

Sodium bicarbonate, 5% solution; 50 g $NaHCO_3$/liter

Sodium bicarbonate, saturated solution; 125 g $NaHCO_3$/liter

Sodium bromide, 0.1 M; 10.3 g NaBr/liter

Sodium carbonate, 0.020 M, 2.1 g Na_2CO_3/liter

Sodium carbonate, 0.1 M; 10.6 g Na_2CO_3/liter

Sodium chloride, 0.020 M, 1.2 g NaCl/liter

Sodium chloride, 0.1 M; 5.85 g NaCl/liter

Sodium chloride, saturated; 60 g NaCl/liter

Sodium hydroxide, 0.020 M, 0.80 g NaOH/liter

Sodium hydroxide, 1.25 M; 50. g NaOH/liter

Sodium hydroxide, 10% solution; 111 g NaOH/liter

Sodium hydroxide, 1% solution; 11.1 g NaOH/liter

Sodium hydroxide, 0.1 M; 4 g NaOH/liter

Sodium hydroxide, 1.25 M, 50. g NaOH/liter

Sodium hydroxide, 0.4 M; 16 g NaOH/liter

Sodium iodide, 0.1 M; 15.0 g NaI/liter

Sodium nitrite, 0.1 M; 6.9 g $NaNO_2$/liter

Sodium phosphate, 0.1 M; 38.0 g $Na_3PO_4 \cdot 12\ H_2O$/liter

Sodium sulfate, 0.1 M; 14.2 g Na_2SO_4/liter

Starch, 1 % solution; 5 g/500 mL (Make slurry and disperse in hot water.)

Sucrose, 1% solution; 10 g sucrose ($C_{12}H_{22}O_{11}$)/liter (freshly prepared)

Sulfuric acid, concentrated; concentrated reagent H_2SO_4

Sulfuric acid, dilute, 9 M; carefully, with stirring, slowly add 500 mL concentrated H_2SO_4 to 400 mL H_2O, cool and dilute to 1 liter

Sulfuric acid, dilute, 3 M; 167 mL concentrated H_2SO_4/liter

Vinegar, commercial (colorless), $HC_2H_3O_2$

Wine, commercial red

Xylose, 1% solution; 1.0 g xylose/100 mL

Zinc nitrate, 0.1 M; 29.8 g $Zn(NO_3)_2 \cdot 6\ H_2O$/liter

Zinc sulfate, 0.2 M; 14.4 g $ZnSO_4 \cdot 7\ H_2O$/250 mL

APPENDIX 3

Special Equipment or Preparations Needed

Experiment 1.   Laboratory Techniques

A small sample of solid lead(II) iodide and sodium nitrate are needed for comparison purposes only.

Experiment 2.   Measurements

An assortment of metal slugs or other solid objects are needed as unknowns for density determination. The diameter of the slugs should be such that they will fit into the 50 mL graduated cylinder. Suggested materials are aluminum, brass, magnesium, steel, etc. Slugs should be numbered for identification.

Experiment 3.   Preparation and Properties of Oxygen

Three demonstrations are suggested (see experiment for details). Büchner funnel-vacuum flask setup for disposal of waste MnO_2.

Experiment 4.   Preparation and Properties of Hydrogen

For safety: Instructor should dispense sodium metal (size of pieces should be no larger than a 4 mm cube).

Experiment 5.   Calorimetry and Specific Heat

An assortment of metal objects like those used for the density determinations in Exp. 2 are needed. They must be small enough to fit into the test tube with id = 22 mm. Styrofoam cups and cardboard cut into 4" squares with a small thermometer hole in the middle should also be available.

Experiment 6.   Freezing Points—Graphing of Data

Slotted corks or stoppers, crushed ice

Experiment 7.   Water in Hydrates

An assortment of samples for unknowns for determination of percent water is needed. Samples can be issued in small coin envelopes or plastic vials. See the Instructor's Manual for the suggested list of samples.

Experiment 8.   Water, Solutions, and pH

The dark blue ice cubes are made by adding methylene blue to tap water until the color is a deep blue. The resulting solution is then frozen in an ice cube tray (Station A6). The green and red colored water is made by adding the food coloring paste to tap water until the result-ing solution is brightly colored (Station A4). Much more red water will be needed than green water. The five lengths of capillary tubing needed should have inner diameter measurements that are different depending on what is available. Example: five tubes with i.d. from among the following: 1.0 mm, 1.5 mm, 2.0 mm, 2.5 mm, 3.0 mm, 3.5 mm; or 0.5 mm, 1.0mm, 1.25 mm, 1.75 mm, 2.75 mm; small electric table fan, 1000 mL beaker or battery jar; micropipettes (Pipetman), 200 μL and 1000 μL with disposable tips.

A series of stations is set up for Sections A1-7 and B 3 #6 instead of each student setting up each activity separately at their own lab bench. A station for measuring pH with a pH meter (B3 #6) is recommended. The other B sections of the experiment can be completed by all students at their own place on the bench. The stations needed are:

Station #	Title of the Experiment/ Observation	Materials needed
Station Al	Molecular Structure & Polarity of Water	Ball and stick molecular model kits (2 or 3 should suffice)
Station A2	Polarity of water and Hydrogen Bonds Between Water Molecules	Buret filled with water, 250 mL beaker, plastic rod (even a smooth plastic ruler will work) and soft rayon or silk cloth.
Station A3	Cohesion and Surface Tension	Clean glass microscope slides, dropping bottles of distilled water and 95% ethanol, and liquid detergent; culture dishes, forceps, common pins
Station A4	Capillarity, Cohesion and Adhesion	5 in. pieces of glass capillary tub-ing with increasing i.d. measure-ments taped to a white index card with at least 1 inch of the tubes extending beyond the bottom edge of the card; a shallow dish of green water, metric rulers.
Station A5 #1-5	Specific Heat (may want to provide three or four of this station since it takes more time than the other activities)	Two 250. mL Erlenmeyer flasks w/2-hole rubber stoppers inserted; thermometers inserted into one hole; large hot plate; two 600 mL beakers
Station A5, #6	Heat of Vaporization	Two thermometers, riag stand, buret clamp, cotton or rayon tubing to cover the thermometer bulbs; table fan
Station A6.	Water Temperature and Density	1000 mL beaker or battery jar, warm tap water, cold red tap water (pre-mixed, refrigerated to 4°C) 10 mL graduated pipet, pipet pump, blue ice cubes, tongs or gloves

(continued)

Appendix 3 (continued)

Station A7.	Density and volume	Electronic balance with at least 0.001 g precision, weigh boats (1"), micropipettes (Pipetman, 200 μL and 1000 μL), disposable pipet tips
Station B 3 #6	Measurement of pH using a pH Meter	Several pH meters so several students can measure pH for these solutions at the same time. If students are unfamiliar with the use of a pH meter, a card with instructions for use should be with each instrument

Experiment 13.   Ionization—Electrolytes and pH

Conductivity apparatus is needed for the demonstration. The procedure is based on the apparatus described in the experiment but other types may be used without detracting from the results of the demonstration. A magnetic stirrer greatly facilitates the last part of the demonstrations. Two or three pH meters are recommended for student use, set up at stations with the solutions described in the experiment.

Experiment 14.   Identification of Selective Anions

Two unknown solutions (in test tubes) are to be issued to each student. Stock reagents used in the experiment are satisfactory for unknowns. See Instructor's Manual for details.

Experiment 16.   Electromagnetic Energy and Spectroscopy

Hand-held spectroscopes, 1.75 m springs for simulating wave motion (1 per 5 students), vapor lamps with power supplies (2 hydrogen and 2 neon); spectrum chart, incandescent and fluorescent lights, spectrophotometers with range from 350-700 nm, colored pencils, meter sticks, stopwatches (recommended). See Instructor's Manual for more details.

Experiment 17.   Lewis Structures and Molecular Models

Ball-and-stick molecular model sets. Two students can share one kit. The number of sets required depends on how many labs are run simultaneously. It is also possible to purchase a large class set of components and divide them into smaller custom kits.

Experiment 18.   Boyle's Law

Boyle's law apparatus is needed. The kits for this experiment can be purchased from several vendors as "Simple Form Boyle's Law Apparatus" or "Elasticity of Gases Kit." The kits include the silicone grease but not the applied weights and vernier calipers. Slotted masses of 0.5 kg and 1 kg allow the applied weights to lie flat on the platform. If not enough slotted masses are available, a combination of bricks and slotted masses works well. One balance per laboratory with the capacity for weighing the heaviest mass to three significant figures. All masses can be preweighed and labeled with tape displaying their mass.

Appendix 3 (continued)

Experiment 20. Liquids—Vapor Pressure and Boiling Points

125 mL flasks containing acetone, methanol, ethanol, and water are needed for Part A. It is suggested that students work in pairs in Part B. A 1-gallon metal can is needed for the demonstration in Part C.

Experiment 21. Molar Volume of a Gas

A 3.0 cc or 5.0 cc disposable syringe is needed for each setup. Needle-rubber stopper assemblies that contain a rubber stopper and syringe needle should be preassembled and checked out and in by students. An additional safety feature is to snip off the end of the needle with a wire cutter after it is in the stopper. The needles need to be heavy enough to push through a rubber stopper without bending. 2 L beakers or battery jars. Büchner funnel-vacuum flask setup needed for disposal of MnO_2.

Experiment 22. Neutralization—Titration I

The following are needed by each student: A small vial or test tube containing about 4 grams of potassium hydrogen phthalate (KHP) (these vials are collected for reuse), one 25 or 50 mL buret, a buret clamp, and 250 mL of unknown NaOH molarity. The NaOH solution is used in Experiments 22 and 23. See Instructor's Manual for details.

Experiment 23. Neutralization—Titration II

The following are needed by each student: A 10 mL volumetric pipet, one 25 or 50 mL buret, 50 mL of acid solution of unknown molarity, 50 mL of vinegar, and 125 mL of standard NaOH solution if Experiment 22 is not done. See Instructor's Manual for details.

Experiment 25. Heat of Reaction

Styrofoam cups are needed.

Experiment 26. Distillation of Volatile Liquids

Distillation setup using a 125 mL or 250 mL flask (see Figure 26.1); hot plates or heating mantles (with rheostats). Red wine as the alcoholic beverage for distillation. Pot holders or mitts to handle hot plate.

Experiment 27. Boiling Points and Melting Points

Boiling point and melting point apparatus (see experiment for details), 200°–250°C thermometers, wire stirrers, capillary melting point tubes, and unknown solids are required. See Instructor's Manual for details.

Experiment 28. Hydrocarbons

Lumps of calcium carbide are needed. Test kerosene to see if it is free of alkenes. Toluene is *not* reacted with bromine.

Experiment 29. Alcohols, Esters, Aldehydes, and Ketones

Furnish No. 18 copper wire with five or six spiral turns at one end. Wire should be about 20 cm overall in length.

Experiment 30. Esterification—Distillation: Synthesis of n-Butyl Acetate

This is a two laboratory period experiment. Reflux and distillation equipment (see experiment for details), 200°–250°C thermometer, and 250 mL separatory funnel are required. If available, a heat source without open flame such as a hot plate or heating mantle with rheostat is recommended. See Experiment 26 for this setup.

Experiment 31. Synthesis of Aspirin

Büchner funnel, suction flask, suction tubing, melting point apparatus, and capillary melting point tubes are needed.

Experiment 32. Amines and Amides

An ice bath is needed to cool the dye reaction.

Experiment 33. Polymers—Macromolecules

Benzoyl peroxide is a shock and heat sensitive material. It should be dispensed to each student by the instructor or by qualified stock room personnel.

Experiment 34. Carbohydrates

Pure fresh or frozen fruit juices, such as orange, lemon, lime, grapefruit, and apple are needed.

Experiment 35. Glucose Concentration in Sheep Blood

Spectrophotometer, 10 mL graduated pipets, 20 mm diameter marbles, protective gloves, and sheep blood are needed. Safe handling of all blood and body fluids must be stressed.

Experiment 37. Paper Chromatography

Five hundred mL Erlenmeyer flasks, 14 × 14 cm squares Whatman No. 1 filter paper, 7 × 7 cm squares of Al foil, hair dryer, micropipets and a spray applicator for ninhydrin are needed. An unknown amino acid or amino acid mixture is required for each student.

Appendix 3 (continued)

Experiment 38. Ion-Exchange Chromatography

Chromatography columns (see experiment for details), Dowex-50 resin slurry, and 600 mL beakers must be provided.

Experiment 39. Identification of an Unknown Amino Acid by Titration

pH meter, pH 7.0 buffer, and magnetic stirrer are needed. An unknown amino acid is issued to each student or student pair.

Experiment 40. Enzymatic Catalysis—Catalase

A potato is needed for each student or student pair. A blender is needed to homogenize the potato/water mixture for preparation of catalase. Büchner funnel filtering setup; cheese cloth.

Experiment 42. Cholesterol Levels in Sheep Blood

Sheep blood, spectrophotometer, centrifuge, centrifuge tubes, 1 mL and 5 mL graduated pipets, and protective gloves are needed. Safe handling of all blood and body fluids should be stressed.

APPENDIX 4

Units of Measurements

Numerical Value of Prefixes with Units

Prefix	Symbol	Number	Power of 10
mega	M	1,000,000	1×10^6
kilo	k	1,000	1×10^3
hecto	h	100	1×10^2
deca	da	10	1×10^1
deci	d	0.1	1×10^{-1}
centi	c	0.01	1×10^{-2}
milli	m	0.001	1×10^{-3}
micro	μ	0.000001	1×10^{-6}
nano	n	0.000000001	1×10^{-9}

Conversion of Units

1 m	=	1000 mm
1 cm	=	10 mm
2.54 cm	=	1 in.
453.6 g	=	1 lb
1 kg	=	2.2 lb, 1000 g
1 g	=	1000 mg
1 L	=	1000 mL
1 mL	=	1 cm^3
0.946 L	=	1 qt
1 cal	=	4.184 J
1 Torr	=	1 mm Hg
760 torr	=	1 atm

Metric Abbreviations

meter	m
centimeter	cm
millimeter	mm
nanometer	nm
liter	L
milliliter	mL
kilogram	kg
gram	g
milligram	mg
mole	mol

Temperature Conversion Formulas

$$°C = \frac{(°F - 32)}{1.8}$$

$$°F = 1.8 \, °C + 32$$

$$K = °C + 273$$

APPENDIX 5

Solubility Table

	$C_2H_3O_2^-$	AsO_4^{3-}	Br^-	CO_3^{2-}	Cl^-	CrO_4^{2-}	OH^-	I^-	NO_3^-	$C_2O_4^{2-}$	O^{2-}	PO_4^{3-}	SO_4^{2-}	S^{2-}	SO_3^{2-}
Al^{3+}	aq	I	aq	–	aq	–	I	aq	aq	–	I	I	aq	d	–
NH_4^+	aq	aq	aq	aq	aq	aq	aq	aq	aq	aq	–	aq	aq	aq	aq
Ba^{2+}	aq	I	aq	I	aq	I	sl. aq	aq	aq	I	sl. aq	I	I	d	I
Bi^{3+}	–	sl. aq	d	I	d	–	I	I	d	I	I	sl. aq	d	I	–
Ca^{2+}	aq	I	aq	I	aq	aq	I	aq	aq	I	I	I	I	d	I
Co^{2+}	aq	I	aq	I	aq	I	I	aq	aq	I	I	I	aq	I	I
Cu^{2+}	aq	I	aq	I	aq	I	I	–	aq	I	I	I	aq	I	–
Fe^{2+}	aq	I	aq	sl. aq	aq	–	I	aq	aq	I	I	I	aq	I	sl. aq
Fe^{3+}	I	I	aq	I	aq	I	I	–	aq	aq	I	I	aq	I	–
Pb^{2+}	aq	I	I	I	I	I	I	I	aq	I	I	I	I	I	I
Mg^{2+}	aq	d	aq	I	aq	aq	I	aq	aq	I	I	I	aq	d	sl. aq
Hg_2^{2+}	sl. aq	I	I	I	I	sl. aq	–	I	aq	I	I	I	I	I	–
Hg^{2+}	aq	I	I	I	aq	sl. aq	I	I	aq	I	I	I	d	I	–
K^+	aq	aq	aq	aq	aq	aq	aq	aq	aq	aq	aq	aq	aq	aq	aq
Ag^+	sl. aq	I	I	I	I	I	–	I	aq	I	I	I	I	I	I
Na^+	aq	aq	aq	aq	aq	aq	aq	aq	aq	aq	aq	aq	aq	aq	aq
Zn^{2+}	aq	I	aq	I	aq	I	I	aq	aq	I	I	I	aq	I	I

Key: aq = Soluble in water   I = Insoluble in water (less than 1 g/100 g H_2O)
      sl. aq = Slightly soluble in water   d = Decomposes in water

APPENDIX 6

Vapor Pressure of Water

Temperature (°C)	Vapor Pressure torr (or mm Hg)	Temperature (°C)	Vapor Pressure torr (or mm Hg)
0	4.6	26	25.2
5	6.5	27	26.7
10	9.2	28	28.3
15	12.8	29	30.0
16	13.6	30	31.8
17	14.5	40	55.3
18	15.5	50	92.5
19	16.5	60	149.4
20	17.5	70	233.7
21	18.6	80	355.1
22	19.8	90	525.8
23	21.2	100	760.0
24	22.4	110	1074.6
25	23.8		

APPENDIX 7

Boiling Points of Liquids

Liquid	Boiling Point °C
Acetone	56.5
Ethanol	78.4
Diethyl ether	34.6
Methanol	64.7
1-propanol	82.5
Water	100.0

APPENDIX 6

Vapor Pressure of Water

Temperature (°C)	Vapor Pressure torr (or mm Hg)	Temperature (°C)	Vapor Pressure torr (or mm Hg)
0	4.6	26	25.2
5	6.5	27	26.7
10	9.2	28	28.3
15	12.8	29	30.0
16	13.6	30	31.8
17	14.5	40	55.3
18	15.5	50	92.5
19	16.5	60	149.4
20	17.5	70	233.7
21	18.6	80	355.1
22	19.8	90	525.8
23	21.2	100	760.0
24	22.4	110	1074.6
25	23.8		

APPENDIX 7

Boiling Points of Liquids

Liquid	Boiling Point °C
Acetone	56.5
Ethanol	78.4
Diethyl ether	34.6
Methanol	64.7
1-propanol	82.5
Water	100.0

APPENDIX 8

Waste Disposal Requirements for Each Experiment

Listed below are special waste containers specified in the experiments for student disposal of waste. Where students are instructed to dispose of wastes in the sink, or where the experiment does not generate waste, the requirements are listed as NONE.

We use the same Waste Heavy Metal bottle for many experiments by combining all the ions poured into it on the label. The same can be done for Organic Solvent Waste bottles.

Exp	Title	Waste Containers That Should Be Available to Students	
1	Laboratory Techniques	Waste Heavy Metals (Pb^+)	bottle
		Waste PbI_2 on filter paper	jar
		Waste or broken glass	Container
2	Measurements	None	
3	Prep. and Prop. of Oxygen	Recycled 9% H_2O_2, unreacted	bottle
		Büchner funnel-vacuum flask	
		for disposal of waste MnO_2	jar
4	Prep. and Prop. of Hydrogen	Recycled Mossy Zinc, rinsed	jar
		unreacted metal strips	jar
5	Calorimetery and Specific Heat	None	
6	Freezing Points	Waste Acetic/Benzoic Acid Mixture	bottle
7.	Water in Hydrates	Waste Heavy Metal Residues (Cu^{2+}, Zn^{2+}, Sr^{2+}, Ba^{2+})	jar
8	Water, Solutions and pH.	Waste Organic Solvents (decane)	bottle
9	Properties of Solutions	Waste Organic Solvent (decane)	bottle
		Waste Kerosene Mixtures	bottle
		Waste Heavy Metal Solutions (Ba^{2+})	bottle
10	Composition of Potassium Chlorate	Waste Heavy Metals (Ag^+)	bottle
		Unused $KClO_3$	bottle
11	Double Displacement Reactions	Waste Heavy Metals (Ag^+, Ba^{2+}, Cu^{2+}, Zn^{2+})	bottle

Appendix 8 (continued)

Exp	Title	Waste Containers That Should Be Available to Students	
12	Single Displacement Reactions	Waste Heavy Metals $(Ag^+, Cu^{2+}, Pb^{2+}, Zn^{2+})$	bottle
13	Ionization—Electrolytes and pH	None (Students do not handle the heavy metal solutions in the demonstration.)	
14	Identification of Selected Anions	Waste Organic Solvents (decane) Waste Heavy Metals (Ag^+, Ba^{2+})	bottle bottle
15	Quantitative Preparation of KCl	None	
16	EM Energy and Spectroscopy	Waste Heavy Metals (Ni^{2+}, MnO_4^-)	bottle
17	Lewis Structures/Molecular Models	None	
18	Boyle's Law	None	
19	Charles' Law	None	
20	Liquids—Vapor Pressure and Boiling Points	None	
21	Molar Volume of a Gas	Büchner funnel-vacuum flask for disposal of the MnO_2 and filter paper. Waste basket	
22	Neutralization—Titration I	None	
23	Neutralization—Titration II	None	
24	Chemical Equilibrium	Waste Heavy Metals (Ag^+, Co^{2+}, Cu^{2+})	bottle
25	Heat of Reaction	None	
26	Distillation of Volatile Liquids	Recycled Ethanol/Ethanol Distillate	bottle
27	Boiling Points and Melting Points	Waste Organic Solvents Used melting point tubes	bottle jar
28	Hydrocarbons	Waste Organic Solvents Waste Heavy Metals (Ag)	bottle bottle

Exp	Title	Waste Containers That Should Be Available to Students	
29	Alcohols, Esters, Aldehydes, Ketones	Waste Organic Solvents	bottle
		Waste Heavy metals (MnO_4^- Ag^+)	bottle
30	Esterification—Distillation	Waste Organic Solvents	bottle
		Solid wastes	jar
31	Synthesis of Aspirin	none	
32	Amines and Amides	Waste Organic Solvents	bottle
33	Polymers—Macromolecules	Waste Organic Solvents	bottle
		Solid waste (nylon and Lucite)	jar
34	Carbohydrates	Molisch test	bottle
		Seliwanoff test	bottle
		Benedict and Barfoed tests	bottle
		Bial test	bottle
		Dehydration (carbon)	jar
35	Glucose Concentration in Blood	Filter paper waste	jar
		Arsenic waste	bottle
36	Amino Acids and Proteins	Biuret test (Cu^{2+})	bottle
		Tyrosine and Ninhydrin tests	bottle
		Waste heavy metals (Pb^{2+})	bottle
		Solid wastes	jar
37	Paper Chromatography	Waste Organic Solvents	bottle
		Solid waste	jar
38	Ion-Exchange Chromatography	Waste Organic Solvents	bottle
		Used resin (for recycling)	jar
39	Unknown Amino Acid by Titration	none	
40	Enzyme Catalysis—Catalase	none	
41	Lipids	Waste Organic Solvents	bottle
		Solid wastes	jar
42	Cholesterol Level in Blood	RBC solids	jar

Periodic Table of the Elements

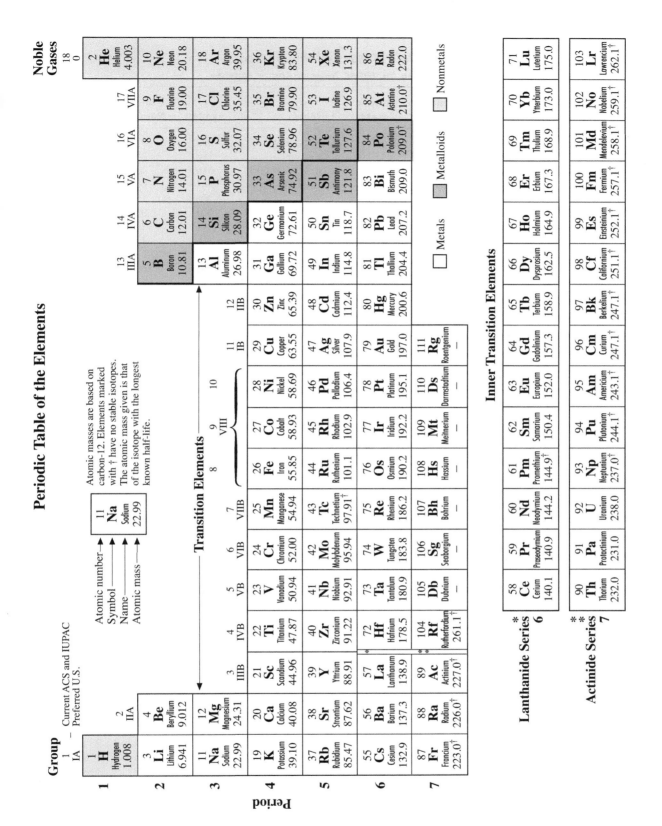

Atomic Masses of the Elements
Based on the IUPAC Table of Atomic Masses

Name	Symbol	Atomic Number	Atomic Mass	Name	Symbol	Atomic Number	Atomic Mass
Actinium*	Ac	89	227	Mendelevium*	Md	101	258
Aluminum	Al	13	26.981538	Mercury	Hg	80	200.59
Americium*	Am	95	243	Molybdenum	Mo	42	95.94
Antimony	Sb	51	121.760	Neodymium	Nd	60	144.24
Argon	Ar	18	39.948	Neon	Ne	10	20.1797
Arsenic	As	33	74.92160	Neptunium*	Np	93	237
Astatine*	At	85	210	Nickel	Ni	28	58.6934
Barium	Ba	56	137.327	Niobium	Nb	41	92.90638
Berkelium*	Bk	97	247	Nitrogen	N	7	14.00674
Beryllium	Be	4	9.012182	Nobelium*	No	102	259
Bismuth	Bi	83	208.98038	Osmium	Os	76	190.23
Bohrium*	Bh	107	264	Oxygen	O	8	15.9994
Boron	B	5	10.811	Palladium	Pd	46	106.42
Bromine	Br	35	79.904	Phosphorus	P	15	30.973762
Cadmium	Cd	48	112.411	Platinum	Pt	78	195.078
Calcium	Ca	20	40.078	Plutonium*	Pu	94	244
Californium*	Cf	98	251	Polonium*	Po	84	209
Carbon	C	6	12.0107	Potassium	K	19	39.0983
Cerium	Ce	58	140.116	Praseodymium	Pr	59	140.90765
Cesium	Cs	55	132.90545	Promethium*	Pm	61	145
Chlorine	Cl	17	35.4527	Protactinium	Pa	91	231.03588
Chromium	Cr	24	51.9961	Radium*	Ra	88	226
Cobalt	Co	27	58.933200	Radon*	Rn	86	222
Copper	Cu	29	63.546	Rhenium	Re	75	186.207
Curium*	Cm	96	247	Rhodium	Rh	45	102.90550
Darmstadtium*	Ds	110	271	Roentgenium*	Rg	111	272
Dubnium*	Db	105	262	Rubidium	Rb	37	85.4678
Dysprosium	Dy	66	162.50	Ruthenium	Ru	44	101.07
Einsteinium*	Es	99	252	Rutherfordium	Rf	104	261.1089
Erbium	Er	68	167.26	Samarium	Sm	62	150.36
Europium	Eu	63	151.964	Scandium	Sc	21	44.955910
Fermium*	Fm	100	257	Seaborgium*	Sg	106	266
Fluorine	F	9	18.9984032	Selenium	Se	34	78.96
Francium*	Fr	87	223	Silicon	Si	14	28.0855
Gadolinium	Gd	64	157.25	Silver	Ag	47	107.8682
Gallium	Ga	31	69.723	Sodium	Na	11	22.989770
Germanium	Ge	32	72.61	Strontium	Sr	38	87.62
Gold	Au	79	196.96655	Sulfur	S	16	32.066
Hafnium	Hf	72	178.49	Tantalum	Ta	73	180.9479
Hassium*	Hs	108	277	Technetium*	Tc	43	98
Helium	He	2	4.002602	Tellurium	Te	52	127.60
Holmium	Ho	67	164.93032	Terbium	Tb	65	158.92534
Hydrogen	H	1	1.00794	Thallium	Tl	81	204.3833
Indium	In	49	114.818	Thorium	Th	90	232.0381
Iodine	I	53	126.90447	Thulium	Tm	69	168.93421
Iridium	Ir	77	192.217	Tin	Sn	50	118.710
Iron	Fe	26	55.845	Titanium	Ti	22	47.867
Krypton	Kr	36	83.80	Tungsten	W	74	183.84
Lanthanum	La	57	138.9055	Uranium	U	92	238.0289
Lawrencium*	Lr	103	262	Vanadium	V	23	50.9415
Lead	Pb	82	207.2	Xenon	Xe	54	131.29
Lithium	Li	3	6.941	Ytterbium	Yb	70	173.04
Lutetium	Lu	71	174.967	Yttrium	Y	39	88.90585
Magnesium	Mg	12	24.3050	Zinc	Zn	30	65.39
Manganese	Mn	25	54.938049	Zirconium	Zr	40	91.224
Meitnerium*	Mt	109	268				

*This element has no stable isotopes. The atomic mass given is that of the isotope with the longest known half-life.

NAMES, FORMULAS AND CHARGES OF COMMON IONS

	Positive Ions (Cations)		Negative Ions (Anions)	
1+	Ammonium	NH_4^+	Acetate	$C_2H_3O_2^-$
	Copper(I)	Cu^+	Bromate	BrO_3^-
	(Cuprous)		Bromide	Br^-
	Hydrogen	H^+	Chlorate	ClO_3^-
	Potassium	K^+	Chloride	Cl^-
	Silver	Ag^+	Chlorite	ClO_2^-
	Sodium	Na^+	Cyanide	CN^-
2+	Barium	Ba^{2+}	Fluoride	F^-
	Cadmium	Cd^{2+}	Hydride	H^-
	Calcium	Ca^{2+}	Hydrogen carbonate	HCO_3^-
	Cobalt(II)	Co^{2+}	(Bicarbonate)	
	Copper(II)	Cu^{2+}	Hydrogen sulfate	HSO_4^-
	(Cupric)		(Bisulfate)	
	Iron(II)	Fe^{2+}	Hydrogen sulfite	HSO_3^-
	(Ferrous)		(Bisulfite)	
	Lead(II)	Pb^{2+}	Hydroxide	OH^-
	Magnesium	Mg^{2+}	Hypochlorite	ClO^-
	Manganese(II)	Mn^{2+}	Iodate	IO_3^-
	Mercury(II)	Hg^{2+}	Iodide	I^-
	(Mercuric)		Nitrate	NO_3^-
	Nickel(II)	Ni^{2+}	Nitrite	NO_2^-
	Tin(II)	Sn^{2+}	Perchlorate	ClO_4^-
	(Stannous)		Permanganate	MnO_4^-
	Zinc	Zn^{2+}	Thiocyanate	SCN^-
3+	Aluminum	Al^{3+}	Carbonate	CO_3^{2-}
	Antimony(III)	Sb^{3+}	Chromate	CrO_4^{2-}
	Arsenic(III)	As^{3+}	Dichromate	$Cr_2O_7^{2-}$
	Bismuth(III)	Bi^{3+}	Oxalate	$C_2O_4^{2-}$
	Chromium(III)	Cr^{3+}	Oxide	O^{2-}
	Iron(III)	Fe^{3+}	Peroxide	O_2^{2-}
	(Ferric)		Silicate	SiO_3^{2-}
	Titanium(III)	Ti^{3+}	Sulfate	SO_4^{2-}
	(Titanous)		Sulfide	S^{2-}
			Sulfite	SO_3^{2-}
4+	Manganese(IV)	Mn^{4+}	Arsenate	AsO_4^{3-}
	Tin(IV)	Sn^{4+}	Borate	BO_3^{3-}
	(Stannic)		Phosphate	PO_4^{3-}
	Titanium(IV)	Ti^{4+}	Phosphide	P^{3-}
	(Titanic)		Phosphite	PO_3^{3-}
5+	Antimony(V)	Sb^{5+}		
	Arsenic(V)	As^{5+}		

The anion charge groupings: **1−** (Acetate through Thiocyanate), **2−** (Carbonate through Sulfite), **3−** (Arsenate through Phosphite).